FORENSIC SCIENCE
A Geek's Guide

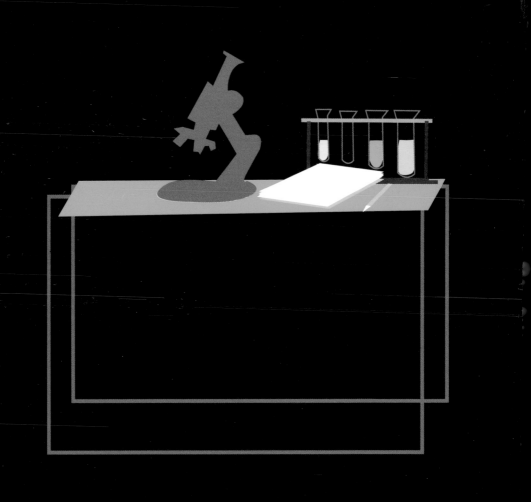

FORENSIC SCIENCE

A Geek's Guide

Steven Morris

BARNES
& NOBLE

NEW YORK

This 2007 edition published by Barnes & Noble, Inc. by arrangement with MQ Publications Limited.

ISBN-13: 978-0-7607-8995-7
ISBN-10: 0-7607-8995-9

1 3 5 7 9 10 8 6 4 2

Printed in Korea

Contents

From the author

The lure of forensic science lies in its remarkable exploration of boundaries and the finding of clues, often abundantly present at a crime scene. Then it's about telling the tale of what happened. As a true crime writer and publisher my avid interest in such a fascinating area of scientific development has certainly fuelled the writing of this book and in the pages that follow you will read about the hundreds of cases I have specifically researched for it. They are the most riveting and informative among the never-ending plethora of chronicled forensic advancement and they include some of the most notorious, and sometimes horrifying, cases of our time. Writing this book has been a highly enjoyable process for me to say the least. I have been flooded with resources and deluged with information from some very knowledgeable colleagues and friends. My true crime website www.newcriminologist.com is the largest of its kind in the world and has many writers—virtually all of whom are experts in their field—responsible for contributing article after article to the prestigious forty-year-old true crime journal that is *The New Criminologist*, now accessible exclusively online. These include former law enforcement officers—many of the homicide persuasion—judges, lawyers, professors, and pathologists, in fact almost anyone you could think of that moves in such criminological circles. This entertaining and informative book is the ultimate collection of forensic facts and statistics, and if you have any questions about any of the cases documented please feel free to drop me a line at steve.morris@newcriminologist.com

Thank you to. . .

My professional colleagues at TNC and their established thoughts and views have been an invaluable aid in the writing of this book. There are far too many of you to thank personally, though I would like to express particular gratitude to former Florida Deputy Sheriff and Legal Investigator David Taylor, now a highly respected instructor of online homicide training courses. David's faith in me significantly influenced the perspective from which this book was written. I must also mention my resident Organized Crime guru and confidant, John Coughlan, a most valued member of my team at The New Criminologist who has never been too far away with his much sought-after advice and painfully constructive criticism.

Julian Blair, with his vast knowledge of criminal cases, crime detection, and passionate views on offender profiling and aberrant psychology, has remained a source of inspiration. Thanks also to my TNC team mates and friends, Dan Parker, who has been there for me from the beginning, Richie Moran, Paul Cleland, Graham Morby, and Steve Price for his wisdom and encouragement. Steve's keenly embraced philosophy of "larging it," whatever the hurdle, has truly shown me the way forward. And my webmaster Simon Beal, who has made it this far with me, often against imposing obstacles. I applaud him both for his extensive knowledge and unfailing loyalty. Finally, heartfelt thanks to my mother Marilyn Dorrall, for her indispensable support and love, my brother Nick, and my beautiful fiancé Nancy Holloway for their continued belief in this author and his writings.

Introduction

"Wherever he steps, whatever he touches, whatever he leaves, even unconsciously, will serve as silent witness against him. Not only his fingerprints or his footprints, but his hair, the fibers from his clothing, the glass he breaks, the tool mark he leaves, the paint he scratches, the blood or semen he deposits or collects. All of these and more bear mute witness against him. This is evidence that does not forget. It is not confused by the excitement of the moment. It is not absent because human witnesses are, it is factual evidence, physical evidence cannot be wrong, it cannot perjure itself; it cannot be wholly absent, only its interpretation can err. Only human failure to find it, study and understand it can diminish its value."

Paul L. Kirk, 1974

The scientific technique for collecting and examining evidence is called forensic science. Simply put, it is the application of science to the law. Forensic scientists take part in the quest for and examination of any physical evidence that can be used to prove or exclude a relationship between the victim or scene of the crime, and the suspect. Information gathered and interpreted includes fingerprints and footwear, blood and other body fluids, bite marks, trace evidence such as hair and fibers from clothing, flammable substances used to start fires, tire and tool marks, glass, paint, and so on. Other areas for scrutiny comprise questionable documents, firearms and explosives, and the analysis of suspect drugs.

The first person to practice modern forensic medicine in 1598 was an Italian, Fortunatus Fidelis, but it failed to become a recognized branch of medicine until the early nineteenth century.

Dr. Edmund Locard's Exchange Principle, propounded in 1910 when he opened his forensic laboratory, was that anybody involved physically in a crime leaves some tiny trace of his presence and usually takes something away with him. In 1912 Locard solved a case when he examined what was beneath the fingernails of a victim, thereby demonstrating that a supposedly unimportant matter can make all the difference when applied to solving a crime. It matters not how much effort goes into cleaning up a scene where a crime has been committed, something will always be left behind. It might not always be found but it is almost impossible to be involved in a violent act without shedding something. Locard's principle was to be the greatest influence in the development of forensic science.

The field of forensic science has undoubtedly come a very long way since its recorded beginnings in the seven hundreds, when fingerprints were used by the Chinese to determine the identity of clay sculptures and documents. It now plays an important part in uncovering political murders, military and governmental cruelties.

Driven by international tribunals, truth commissions, and nongovernmental organizations, investigations are taking place in more than thirty countries. Investigators are identifying offenders and their victims and demonstrating evidence of genocide and mass murder. This is possible through the use of forensic pathology, archaeology, odontology, anthropology, computer modeling, ballistics, DNA analysis, and in many other areas of forensic science.

All the forensic disciplines involve similar approaches. The aim is to reconstruct previous human activities. In order to suggest probable scenarios, physical remains must be studied, be they objects or corpses.

And still new technologies continue to transform the field of forensic science. In order to reconstruct crimes, scientists are employing advanced techniques such as 3-D computer imaging, mass spectrometry, high-performance liquid chromatography, and of course DNA testing. Cutting-edge forensic science can find organic materials and trace elements down to a level of a few hundred molecules.

But scientists must ensure their evidence is authentic and dependable and can survive under the microscope that is public opinion and in the law courts. It is a sad fact of life that some killers do get away with murder. But today new techniques such as genetic fingerprinting provide the opportunity to trace the killers. Used in a balanced way this science can reveal crimes that have been hidden—convicting the guilty and exonerating the innocent.

The first of the forensic sciences, modern forensic toxicology, dates back about two hundred years. Technically it is the investigation of poisons but it also involves the study of substances present in the body that can have a poisonous effect like illegal drugs, drug overdoses, poisonous gas, alcohol, and industrial chemicals. A typical toxicological activity comprises analysis of hair, or a urine or blood sample. On other occasions an autopsy involving the removal of tissue samples is necessary. Toxicology is essential not only when a crime is suspected but also for suicides and accidental deaths. A forensic toxicologist might be invited to test for anything from thallium to poisonous gas to prescription drugs.

Scientists continue in their researches to come up with new methods of identifying and analyzing chemical substances. Processes are getting more specialized and technologies are uniting to produce ever more sophisticated and sensitive tests.

In the development of ballistics and the comparison of firearms, the microscope was the most important tool in the box. The first rudimentary microscopes appeared in the sixteen hundreds giving a magnification of ten to twenty but the images were sometimes indistinct. With the introduction of the compound microscope which comprised multiple lenses fused together, optics magnification and clarity increased dramatically. Now firearm specialists are able to reproduce erased serial numbers; estimate the exact distance of a shooting; match bullets to a particular firearm and detect gunpowder residue on perpetrators and around wounds.

Then we have the field of forensic odontology, which is the application of medical and dental expertise to legal issues. Forensic odontologists are qualified dentists who have received supplementary training and are able to offer expert testimony on dentistry. Forensic archaeology attempts to identify the environment of the individual being excavated. It is possible to discover when and how graves were dug, the vegetation, geology, and climate—even the season that certain activities took place. This is possible from studying plant fragments and pollen samples. Some species of plant can tell us with reasonable accuracy when a body was buried in the ground. Also the location of a burial can be possible by studying soil samples from a suspect's footwear or clothing. Vegetation and soil can also determine the source of buried drugs, weapons, and explosives.

Trace evidence, usually not enough on its own, often corroborates other evidence. But it is sometimes sufficient to induce a confession. There are many different systems used in their analysis because trace evidence can be anything from a plant fragment to a paint chip to a strand of hair. The reason for this science is that if a seemingly unrelated piece of material or object is found at a crime scene, tracking down its origin can support an arrest and conviction. Also, discovering some trace from the crime scene or victim on a suspect can have a powerful influence on a case. Most examinations focus on hair or fibers, easier to see than dirt or pollen.

Surely a system that appears to improve recollection, thus helping in the apprehension of a criminal, cannot be a bad thing? Although hypnosis has played an important role in criminal cases such as Ted Bundy and Albert DeSalvo, the jury is still out regarding its usefulness. However, no one forensic discipline is as controversial as the employment of a polygraph to detect deception. It is still the subject of heated debate but it is increasingly used in courts of law.

Sir Andrew Maclagan, British Professor of Medicine at Edinburgh University, famously said in 1878, "A dead body tells no tales except those it whispers to the quick ear of the scientific expert, by him to be reported to the proper quarter."

The reason for an autopsy is to examine a dead body and record detailed anatomical peculiarities. Microscopic and clinical study of organs is often required to support the forensic pathologist's conclusions. Unfortunately even the most revered practitioner can be stumped; for example, the strange phenomenon of the "Custody Death Syndrome" where there are "no physical markers (in these deaths), there is no anatomical change, no ruptured heart, no blown aneurism. Typically, the heart and lungs just stop, and that raises all kinds of questions."

Research by medical examiners continues to be undertaken into these strange, unexplained, arrest-related deaths.

Finally the work of forensic biologists in performing scientific analyses of, e.g., saliva, blood, and semen is of crucial use in the investigation of civil and criminal cases. Emerging over the last twenty years or so DNA analysis has become an indispensable way of identifying both victims and suspects of crime.

My objective in the compilation of this work is that anyone curious about, or fascinated by, the subject of forensic science can refer time and again to the contents in order to follow a trail of clues to sometimes startling discoveries; to visit the twisted domain of the psychological killer; to read again of bloody accounts of violent crime. The facts contained in the book are brutal and chilling at times, taking us to deep, dark places, but there is an irresistible urge to find out more about the morbid yet captivating aspects of forensic science.

The area of study for the forensic scientist is broad, variable, and at times capricious. The responsibilities of the forensic scientist are difficult and not without risk as they have to examine physical evidence related to crimes like rape and murder: saliva, blood, firearms, explosives and explosive substances, drugs, alcohol, inflammables like petrol, etc. They have to handle skeletal remains, poisons, hair, animal and plant residues, and weapons used in, for example, arson and burglary. Other disciplines include photographs of physical evidence and the study of forged documents and signatures.

The task of the forensic scientist is to examine precisely any material evidence and determine whether or not it is connected to a specific criminal or crime. In order to ensure evidence is collected in a proper manner, often called to the crime scene to assist in the investigation.

A forensic toxicologist, whether or not the case is one of suicide or homicide, examines the viscera and other relevant tissues to determine the quantity and quality of the poison used. His report is invaluable to investigating agencies and to the court.

The role of the forensic biologist often overlaps the work done by, e.g., the toxicologist, the botanist, and the anthropologist. He analyzes biological evidence from microorganisms to higher animals and plants. He studies different types of poisonous plant fragments where plant poison is used in the committing of a crime. In examining skeletal remains, he can provide answers to questions like the age, stature, sex, and origin of the deceased.

FORENSIC PHARMACOLOGY

Forensic pharmacology is the application of medication sciences to legal issues. Including other professional work, the forensic pharmacologist engages in the criminal justice system.

Some of the issues concerning forensic pharmacology are:
- Pharmacologic euthanasia
- Screening and testing for drugs of abuse
- Drug-induced violence
- Product tampering

- Health care and scientific fraud, quackery
- Poisoning—serving as a toxicologist for the Medical Examiner's office
- Effect of psychoactive drugs on competency to stand trial
- Psychopharmacological effects as a mitigating factor in criminal activity (perhaps resulting in a reduced sentence)
- Working as a criminalist for a police department
- Appointed as a special agent for the FBI

FORENSIC CHEMISTRY

Drug chemists take any controlled substances that are submitted as evidence and determine their purity or whether there has been any substitution of or tampering with commercial/prescription drugs. Tests include: ultraviolet and infrared spectrophotometry and mass spectroscopy, gas and high performance liquid chromatography, and colour and crystal tests to determine whether the evidence comprises illegal or controlled substances.

BALLISTICS

The ballistic expert determines whether or not a specific firearm or ammunitions were used in a crime. He gives his opinion to direction and angle of firing, ranges, and distances. He offers his expertise in explosive substances, which are being used nowadays at an alarming rate.

FORGERIES AND HANDWRITING ANALYSIS

In crimes such as forgery, our handwriting expert studies various types of documents. Besides forged signatures, he gives his opinion on typewritten documents, when they were written, and the probable age of the ink used.

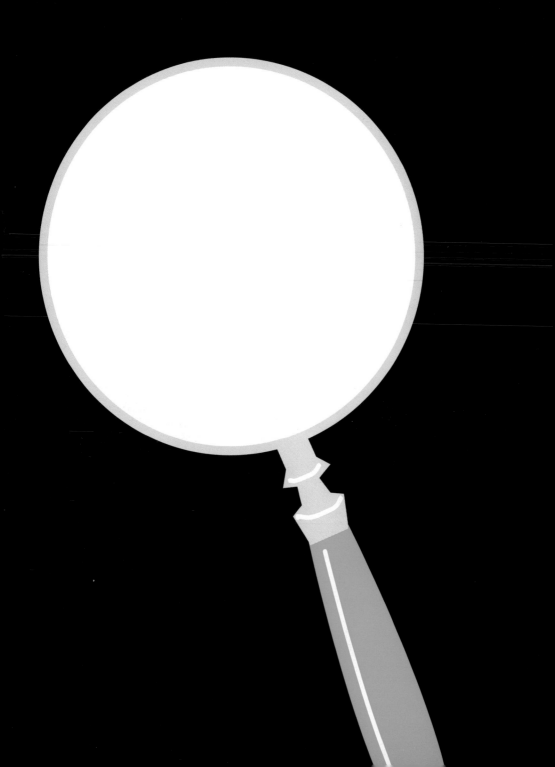

The Early Years and the Washing Away of Wrongs

HSI DUAN YU

In 1248 in China, a book entitled *Hsi Duan Yu* ("the washing away of wrongs") appears. It demonstrates physical differences between the bodies of people who had died of natural and unnatural causes. As far as we know this is the first use of medical knowledge as an instrument for solving crimes.

SEVENTH AD

In the late seventh century AD, during the Chinese T'ang dynasty, Ti Jen-Chieh is said to have used a powerful combination of logic and forensic evidence to solve myriad crimes using a band of investigators who question suspects and witnesses, study the scene of the crime, and examine physical evidence.

Modest Beginnings

Persia, in the 14th century: impressions of fingerprints are featured in government papers of the time.

JANSEN'S COMPOUND MICROSCOPE

Zacharias Jansen invents the compound microscope in 1590. Its use of magnification through two or three separate lenses ultimately allows fingerprints to be examined in much finer detail.

LITTLE FOUNTAINS

Dutch Botanist, Dr. Nehemia Grew composes a paper in 1684 explaining his examination into the patterns of palms and fingers along with the composition of epidermal ridges and sweat pores. He goes on to name the sweat pores "little fountains," not realising that in the future they will be used to identify criminals at crime scenes.

NAMED AFTER HIM

IN 1686 AT BOLOGNA UNIVERSITY IN ITALY, PROFESSOR OF ANATOMY, MARCELLO MALPIGHI IS INVOLVED IN PIONEERING RESEARCH INTO FINGERPRINTING. UNFORTUNATELY HE DID NOT CONNECT FINGERPRINTS AND THEIR IMPORTANCE AS A MEANS OF IDENTIFICATION. A LAYER OF HUMAN SKIN, HOWEVER, IS NAMED AFTER HIM.

INCRIMINATING INFORMATION

Although in these modern times an integral part of every detective story is the matching of evidence found at the crime scene with evidence found on the suspect, it is not until 1784 in Lancaster, England, that John Toms becomes the first person convicted of a crime using this technique. The unfortunate victim in the case is shot dead. A torn piece of newspaper found in Toms's pocket is discovered to match a scrap inside a pistol. This evidence helps find John Toms guilty of murder.

"FATHER OF FINGERPRINTING"

One of the first ever recorded cases where fingerprints are involved in solving a crime takes place in a Tokyo burglary in the 1800s. Dr. Henry Faulds uses his fingerprint technique to exonerate an innocent suspect and convict the perpetrator. Henry Faulds is acknowledged today as the "father of fingerprinting" but it takes until the late twentieth century before his great achievements are duly recognized.

HIS MARK

Thomas Bewick, an English author, naturalist and engraver, in 1818 identifies his work by using engravings of his fingerprints. One of his carvings carries the logo "Thomas Bewick—his mark." This is so carefully reproduced that experts think it credible that Bewick is among the first to understand the uniqueness of a fingerprint.

THE NINE TYPES

In 1823 at Breslau University, Germany, Professor of Anatomy, Johannes Purkinje, delivers a dissertation in which he reports nine types of finger patterns. Crucially, as with Marcello Malpighi before him, he fails to recognize fingerprints as a resource in the identification of an individual.

Exposing impostors

Sir William Herschel, from the Indian Civil Service has, by 1858, for quite a while been considering fingerprints as a method of identification. At the time one of his duties is to oversee the payment of allowances to pensioned Indian soldiers. Unfortunately impersonation is rife and so he has problems preventing this practice. He decides as each soldier receives his payment, to take their fingerprints and he is able to make a distinction between the real petitioners and the impostors.

THE PRINCIPLE OF PERSISTENCY

Over a period spanning sixty years, Sir William Herschel conducts experiments in an effort to prove his Principle of Persistency. This argues that fingerprints are formed whilst still in the womb and they persist throughout life. They are also one of the last features to recede after death has taken place. It is a pity that the Indian Government does not recognize the potential in fingerprint identification in Herschel's report to them. Herschel had argued for their use in identification of prisoners but had never established a method of classification and so it is not introduced until much later.

THE STEREOSCOPIC MICROSCOPE

Optical microscopes with up to two thousand times the magnification are developed by the 1880s. One such, the stereoscopic microscope, has double eye pieces and lens systems which create prisms, providing a three-dimensional image. It is used when viewing paint evidence and making soil comparisons. In 1836 Alfred Swaine Taylor publishes *Elements of Medical Jurisprudence,* which later becomes a classic referral text of forensic medicine.

NATURE

A journal entitled Nature *in October 1880, publishes an article by a Scottish physician by the name of Dr. Henry Faulds. In it he advocates the use of fingerprints as evidence left at a crime scene. "When bloody fingerprints or impressions on clay, glass, etc. exist, they may lead to the scientific identification of criminals. Although I have had experience in two such cases…There can be no doubt as to the advantage of having, beside their photograph a copy of the forever unchangeable finger furrows of important criminals."*

HANS GROSS AND THE *SYSTEM DER KRIMINALISTIK*

Austrian-born Hans Gross is one of criminal detection's most influential figures. First a lawyer and later an examining magistrate, his chief interest lies in applied academic and scientific discipline in the context of crime solution. He is later honored with the chair in criminology at the University of Prague. He also becomes Professor of Penal Law at the University of Graz. His contribution to forensic science is the 1893 publication of his *System der Kriminalistik*, translated as *Criminal Investigation*. This classic textbook encompasses microscopy, fingerprints, and serology, though one of Gross's more notable achievements is in the field of ballistics.

THE INDIAN GOVERNMENT ACCEPTS

A MEMBER OF THE INDIAN CIVIL SERVICE, AS WAS SIR WILLIAM HERSCHEL BEFORE HIM, SIR EDWARD HENRY IN 1896, IS EXPERIMENTING WITH FINGER AND THUMB PRINT TESTING. HE ARRANGES FOR THE COLLECTION OF FINGERPRINTS OF CRIMINALS AND USES THEM TO COME UP WITH A SYSTEM OF CLASSIFICATION. IN 1897 HE IS SUCCESSFUL IN INDUCING THE INDIAN GOVERNMENT TO ACCEPT HIS SYSTEM ON A NATIONAL BASIS.

LORD BELPER'S COMMITTEE

IN 1900 IN GREAT BRITAIN, A COMMITTEE IS FORMED UNDER LORD BELPER. THIS IS INITIATED BECAUSE OF THE PUBLIC'S ALARM CONCERNING WRONGFUL CONVICTIONS AND MISTAKEN IDENTITIES. LORD BELPER AND HIS COMMITTEE ARE REQUIRED TO INVESTIGATE THE DIFFICULTIES OF PERSONAL IDENTIFICATION FOR POLICE PURPOSES. BOTH THE FINGERPRINT CLASSIFICATION METHOD INTRODUCED BY SIR EDWARD HENRY AND THE ANTHROPOMETRIC SYSTEM INVENTED BY BERTILLON ARE ASSESSED FOR THEIR RELATIVE VIRTUES. THEY DECIDE UNANIMOUSLY TO SELECT THE FINGERPRINT SYSTEM DEVISED BY HENRY AND SO IT IS RECEIVED INTO NEW SCOTLAND YARD IN JULY 1901. SIR EDWARD HENRY GOES ON TO BECOME COMMISSIONER OF THE METROPOLITAN POLICE IN 1903. IN THE FUTURE HIS SYSTEM WILL BE USED BY THE REMAINDER OF THE COMMONWEALTH AND IN EUROPEAN COUNTRIES.

CONVICTED BY HENRY'S SYSTEM

In England, on September 13, 1902, the first fingerprint evidence retrieved from the scene of a crime is heard at the Central Criminal Court. Henry Jackson protests his innocence against a charge of burglary at a house in south London and the theft of some billiard balls in June 1902. At the crime scene an imprint of Jackson's thumb is found in dirt on a window-sill. Richard Muir, an eminent barrister of the time, conducts the case for the prosecution. He illustrates Henry's fingerprint system and shows the court photographic enlargements of the print. Jackson is convicted and serves seven years in penal servitude.

TELLING THE WEST TWINS APART

In 1903 the New York State Prison introduces the first regular use of fingerprints to identify criminals in the United States. Will West, a recently arrived prisoner at Leavenworth State Prison, Kansas, is distinguished from another inmate by the same name, by the use of fingerprints. It turns out the two are identical twins.

THE STRATTON'S SWING

The first use of fingerprints as evidence in a murder trial in England takes place in 1905. Mr. and Mrs. Farrow are murdered at their shop in Deptford and Albert and Alfred Stratton deny their involvement. At the scene of the crime an impression is discovered on a cash box. Inspector Collins, in giving his evidence, uses a blackboard and photographic enlargements of the impression lifted from the cash box, to illustrate the fingerprint identification system. He compares a print taken from the right thumb of Alfred Stratton with that on the cash box and demonstrates the match. The jury finds the Strattons guilty of murder and they are subsequently hanged.

IMPORTANT BEGINNINGS

AROUND THE END OF THE EIGHTEENTH CENTURY THE DEVELOPMENT OF MODERN CHEMISTRY IN THE WEST HERALDS THE INTRODUCTION INTO THE COURTROOMS OF SCIENTIFIC AND MEDICAL EXPERTS. IN FRANCE, IN 1910, THE WORLD SEES ITS FIRST FORENSIC LABORATORY, WHILE IN 1930 THE U.S. ESTABLISHES ITS FIRST CRIME LABORATORY AT THE BEHEST OF THE LOS ANGELES COUNTY SHERIFF'S DEPARTMENT. A YEAR LATER THE FBI LABORATORY IS CREATED.

BLOOD GROUP DISCOVERY

IN 1930 KARL LANDSTEINER IS AWARDED THE NOBEL PRIZE FOR HIS DISCOVERY OF HUMAN BLOOD GROUPS. LANDSTEINER PERSEVERES WITH HIS RESEARCH INTO BLOOD, ITS TYPES AND SPECIES AND THIS CONSTITUTES THE BASIS OF NEARLY ALL OTHER RESEARCH IN THIS AREA. MAX RICHTER EMPLOYEES LANDSTEINER'S SYSTEM TO TYPE STAINS IN ONE OF THE FIRST ATTEMPTS TO SPECIFICALLY USE VALIDATION EXPERIMENTS IN ORDER TO ADOPT A TECHNIQUE FOR FORENSIC SCIENCE.

PERSISTENCE

The ridges, ridge detail and patterns of fingerprints grow with the body but they remain constant, never changing throughout life.

IN THE WOMB

Between the third and fifth month of pregnancy when the foetus is about three inches long, ridges start to form.

AFTER DEATH

After death, ridges remain intact, enduring long after most other parts of the body. Even when the flesh is exposed to a state of advanced decomposition, fingerprints are usually still able to be obtained.

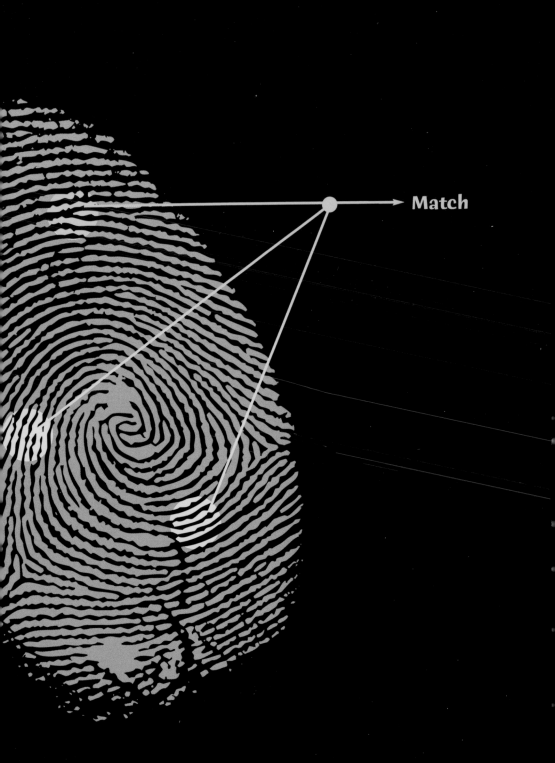

Match

Prints, Impressions, and Voices

"It's never going to be like fingerprints or DNA, but it's another tool in the forensic tool box."

John Kennerley, Chief Fingerprint Officer in the Lancashire, U.K., police force, talking about ear prints

PRINTED IN 1892

In 1892 the notable Sir Francis Galton publishes his book *Fingerprints* which establishes the uniqueness and permanence of fingerprints. It is a most respected work which is regarded as a superlative achievement in forensic circles. The characteristics identified within *Fingerprints* (minutia) are still in use today.

JUAN VUCETICHS AND THE ORIGINS OF FORENSIC FINGERPRINTING

In a village near Buenos Aires, Argentina in 1892, two boys are savagely murdered. The boys' mother, Francisca Rojas, has a boyfriend called Velasques, and he is the prime suspect in the homicides. He protests his innocence vehemently, even under physical torture from his police interrogators.

At the crime scene a bloody fingerprint has been discovered and investigators contact Juan Vucetichs, who is in the process of creating a system of fingerprint identification. Vucetichs compares both the fingerprints of Velasques and Rojas with the bloody print.

It matches Rojas's and she subsequently confesses. This is the first successful use of fingerprint identification in a murder case.

A QUESTION OF GENETICS

It is widely known that fingerprint patterns are inherited. They are formed while still in the womb and throughout life they will never change—even after death they linger for a while! It is because of this very uniqueness that fingerprints are so useful for identification purposes. Under your skin, in a layer called the "dermal papillae," is where fingerprints are formed. Even after burning or scarring (be it accidental or intentional), while the layer of papillae exists, fingerprints will always return.

THE FIRST ALL-AMERICAN FINGERPRINT

In 1910, Clarence Hiller of Chicago discovers an intruder in his home. A scuffle ensues in which Mr Hiller is shot twice and the intruder, Thomas Jennings, escapes into the night. He is apprehended not far from the scene, running and looking furtively behind him, as if on the lookout for pursuers. He is carrying a loaded revolver. Although there are spent cartridges at the house, it is the fingerprints he leaves behind in Mr. Hiller's kitchen that lead to his downfall.

That day Mr. Hiller had painted some railings next to the window via which Jennings gained access to the house. On the still-wet paint is a perfect set of fingerprints that match Jennings's perfectly. The spent shells also match his revolver, but that is mere icing on the cake. Jennings becomes the first American to be convicted on fingerprint evidence.

FINGERPRINTS AND FOOTPRINTS AS EVIDENCE

Arguably the most worthwhile items of evidence at any crime scene are prints left by the hands or bare feet of the suspect. In an investigation the types of prints sought after are:

a) Latent prints: produced by secretions of the skin like sebaceous oil, dirt or perspiration left on an object that has been touched. Easily found on smooth surfaces, if circumstances are favorable, they can also be found on rougher surfaces such as wood, starched material, tightly woven fabrics—even human skin.

b) Patent or visible prints: produced by transferring a substance like grease, ink, dust, blood, to an object that has been touched. A dust print is the most common. At times this print can be so well defined it can be looked for in a single fingerprint file. A successful print can also be obtained when contamination with other substances like paint, soot, flour, and ink takes place. Less dependable are fingerprints in blood.

c) Plastic or molded prints: produced when pressed against a soft surface like soap, wax, putty, and grease —an impression can even be left in a victim's skin.

A FULL CONFESSION

In 1911 Charles Crispi, aka Cesare J. Cella, becomes involved in a murder case—the first case in fact which features fingerprint evidence as the sole form of evidence. Fingerprint expert Joseph Faurot testifies at the ensuing trial and, after hearing Faurot's testimony, Crispi pleads guilty. Asked by the judge for a full confession Crispi acquiesces, ensuring that no further charges are filed against him. The purpose of the judge's request is to test whether the scientific evidence introduced at trial is correct. It is.

AFIS

AFIS stands for "Automated Fingerprint Identification Systems," which enable computers to make rapid and accurate comparisons between individual fingerprints from within the massive amounts of fingerprints that are stored on police fingerprint databases.

EASILY DEVELOPED

It is possible to develop prints from almost any surface. They can be directly developed from skin, (e.g., from the neck of a strangled person), or items that have been immersed under water, and understandably it is easy to obtain them from wood, paper, metal, etc.

LEATHER AND WOOLLEN GLOVES

Just because a perpetrator elects to wear gloves in an attempt to deter his potential detectors from linking him to a crime, it does not always prevent his fingerprints from being left behind. Leather, originally cow hide, which is as individual as human skin when used to make gloves, can yield a print that is unique to that glove alone. Even the print made by a woollen glove can be distinctive enough to be traced back ultimately to the offender.

LATEX GLOVES

Surgical or latex gloves are designed to fit the hand like a second skin and fingerprints can readily "pass through" the thin latex layer. Turning them inside out can also result in fingerprints being found on the inside surfaces of the latex. As a result they are not the most effective precaution a criminal may take in the furtherance of his crime, despite what he thinks he knows from watching the movies!

SUPERGLUE FUMING

This is a method employed for visualizing latent fingerprints on nonporous surfaces by using cyanoacrylate ester fumes.

THE END OF HENRY'S CLASSIFICATION

Gone are the days when the standard technique used to match fingerprints was the "Henry Classification System," an unwieldy series of numbers and letters broken down into various degrees of classification, where it would take weeks, even months to make a comparison between fingerprint files and a suspect's print. The arrival of digital technology has revolutionized all of this. Prints are now scanned directly into a computer, forgoing the need for fingerprint cards and ink. Now prints can be compared at the astonishing rate of four hundred thousand per second!

NOT GUILTY

IN 1968 RICHARD STANLEY KENT IS CHARGED WITH MURDERING AN EX-NEW YORK CITY POLICE OFFICER NAMED JOSEPH MURPHY. THE KEY EVIDENCE AGAINST KENT IS A LATENT FINGERPRINT DISCOVERED ON A HEADBOARD. DR. VASSILIS C. MORFOPOULOS, DIRECTOR OF THE AMERICAN STANDARDS TESTING BUREAU, IS CALLED TO VIEW THE IDENTIFICATION. HE ANALYZES THE IDENTIFICATION USING A 25X MICROSCOPE AND FINDS THREE DIFFERENCES. "ONE DISTINCT AND CRUCIAL DIFFERENCE DESTROYS THE VALIDITY OF AN IDENTIFICATION," HE SAYS, AND RICHARD KENT IS FOUND NOT GUILTY OF THE MURDER. IN 1970, THE FBI AND THE IAI [INTERNATIONAL ASSOCIATION FOR IDENTIFICATION] CHALLENGE DR. MORFOPOULOS'S ANALYSIS.

DR. CAMPS AND THE 4605TH "PALMER"

In April 1955 Dr. Francis Camps confirms that Elizabeth Currell has been battered to death. It also appears as though a botched rape attempt has been made upon her. The killer leaves a solitary clue in his wake, a fragmentary palm print, found on the murder weapon. A subsequent mass palm-printing exercise, encompassing seven thousand homes, is carried out in Potters Bar, U.K.

Nine thousand palm prints, or "palmers," are taken over a four-month period. Experts are midway through comparing them when the 4605th print taken matches that of a seventeen-year-old youth named Michael Queripel. His subsequent trial lasts just five minutes.

DID RANDY KRAFT WORK ALONE?

One of the state of California's worst serial killers, Randall "Randy" Steven Kraft, is convicted in 1989 of sixteen hideous murders involving extreme torture and mutilation. He is strongly suspected of at least another fifty-one homicides. However in two of the cases forensic evidence indicates he was aided by an accomplice. There is semen present in and on the victims that did not match Kraft's DNA and also an extra set of footprints present at some of the crime scenes. In fact, privately, members of the prosecution team admit that they failed to charge Kraft with several murders they were convinced he had committed because of these findings.

THE "JOHN BARLEYCORN" KILLER

In 1943 Harold Loughman, an objectionable killer, murders Miss Rose Robinson, the landlady of the "John Barleycorn" public house in Portsmouth, England. Loughman enters through a back window and strangles her for the night's takings. He leaves behind a small black button with a broken thread. However, it takes a while to prove that Loughman committed this crime despite an actual confession of committing serious thefts and the fact that he has a missing button that matches the one found at the scene of the crime.

The problem is that Loughman has no fingers on his right hand (which explains the lack of fingernail imprints), and the court believes that this disability would deem strangulation an impossibility; therefore the defendent is acquitted. A case cannot be tried twice; so, safe from any further prison sentences, Loughman confesses, "I want to say I done that job. I did kill that woman in the public house in Portsmouth." They should have studied the evidence further.

CATCHING THE NIGHT STALKER

In the mid-1980s twelve brutal murders occur in Los Angeles and the city is held in a grip of fear. The horrific crime scenes are soaked in blood and marked with satanic symbols, but police are still no closer to catching the "Night Stalker." However, a surviving victim of the serial murderer manages to write down the license number of his automobile as he flees the scene. The vehicle is stolen and forensic examiners find a single fingerprint inside. When it is run through the fingerprint database a positive match is found. As it later transpires Richard Ramirez, the man responsible for each of the homicides had had his fingerprints taken following a minor traffic violation some years earlier.

Another frightening multiple killer is whisked off the streets and sentenced to death by lethal injection in 1989.

PERSISTENT PRINTS

One time "Public Enemy Number One" and high-profile outlaw John Dillinger is becoming anxious as the FBI close in on him. He is smart enough to realize that leaving fingerprints at a crime scene can condemn him, so he has an idea. He locates a crooked team of plastic surgeons and pays them five thousand dollars to burn off his fingerprints with acid and change the way he looks physically. As it turns out the "cowboy" surgeons bungle the anaesthetic and Dillinger almost dies during surgery, but at least his fingerprints are gone.

Not long after, he is shot and killed by FBI agents. At the morgue he is examined and his fingerprints taken—this is when the FBI discovers his elaborate attempt at deception. But the surgeons have been unsurprisingly negligent and his fingers still contain enough ridge patterns to positively identify the notorious villain.

TERRORISTS FIRST TARGET THE WORLD TRADE CENTER

In 1993 a yellow truck packed with massive amounts of explosives detonates in a basement parking lot at New York City's World Trade Center. The plan is to blow up one tower so it falls into the other and brings both towers down.

It is a plan that fails although six people are killed and a thousand are injured. The explosion causes five million dollars' worth of damages. Investigators get a break when Mohammad Salameh tries to claim back four hundred dollars from the rental company that owns the truck, claiming it was stolen. The police tail Salameh back to his New Jersey apartment and a nearby storage shed that was used as the bomb factory. The fingerprints of Salameh and three of the other bombers are found there. From this evidence six men are charged and convicted of the bombing.

THE COMPUTER CONNECTION

Computers scan fingerprints discovered at the crime scene, automatically locating and recording arches, loops, ridges, and whorls. The data collected is then compared with similar information already on the database. The computer next creates a shortlist of matches in descending order of probability. Finally, investigators are able to use the short-list to manually compare with the crime scene fingerprint in order to establish any matches.

THE SOLE PIECE OF EVIDENCE

In 1952 a warehouse in Aberdeen, Scotland, is broken into and robbed. A fine cover of dust on the floor reveals imprints of stocking feet. These sole marks indicate broken areas which seem to have arisen from holes in the perpetrator's socks. An early suspect in the robbery is James Walker Adams. Through the holes in the socks there are traces of friction ridges made by the intruder's left and right feet. These impressions are then photographed and compared with Adams's sole prints. Three of the photographs contain respectively seventy-two, thirty-two and forty ridge characteristics with the sole prints of the accused. This is the first case of a person convicted on the evidence of a sole print in a Scottish court.

THE DUDE ABIDES

A man is seen by the occupant of the home he has just burglarized as he attempts to climb out of a bedroom window to make good his escape. Laden as he is with stolen items from the property he is unable to conceal a distinctive tattoo of the word "Dude," visible on his forearm.

The homeowner recognizes the tattoo as belonging to a local laborer known as "Mac," who has an extensive arrest record for theft and assault with the Arizona PD. Knowing that the authorities must surely have Mac's prints on file the owner admonishes him to drop his recently acquired booty and leave before he calls the police.

Foolishly not having worn gloves and knowing that a positive ID will lead to his prints being examined all the quicker, Mac duly submits to the demand and hastily retreats into the darkness. He is arrested anyway!

FEET

Just as with fingerprints, bare feet also have unique prints. "Barefoot morphology," as it is known, has established that the soles of the feet have characteristic ridges, as with finger pads. Also advantageous to identification is the fact that no two people will have the same-shaped foot.

In the case against Charles Manson and his "Family," Los Angeles detectives have little solid evidence to link them undeniably to the murder of popular actress Sharon Tate and several other victims. The outrageous behavior displayed in the courtroom by Manson and his followers may be enough to prejudice the jury against them, but it looks like the chance of gaining convictions are slim.

The LAPD are desperately looking for more evidence to cover the embarrassing fact that they had earlier been given the revolver that killed Tate, and then had inexplicably lost it! The Family members show no remorse and stick to their contrived story—concocted in custody.

The breakthrough comes when a bloody fingerprint found on the wall of Tate's home is identified as that of one of the Manson Family and a wallet found at the scene is identified as Family member Rosemary LaBianca's. The prints on the wall and the wallet help convict multiple Family members.

EAROLOGY

Johann Lavater initiates a practice called earology based on the individual design of the ear, almost one hundred years before fingerprints are used as identification. Today there is a computer database in the United Kingdom comprising some several thousand ear prints.

FOOTPRINTS AND IMPRESSIONS

In 1816 in Warwick, England, a young maidservant is found drowned in a shallow pool. She is the victim of a most brutal assault. At the crime scene police find some grains of wheat and chaff but, perhaps more importantly, in the moist earth by the pool, footprints and an impression from corduroy cloth with a sewn patch. A farm laborer had earlier been threshing wheat in the vicinity and his trousers are taken from him and examined. They are found to match the impression made in the earth and he is summarily tried and convicted of murder.

IF PROPERLY DEALT WITH

In the past footwear evidence has been largely disregarded, mainly for two reasons: a) the evidence is incorrectly interpreted or underestimated and b) poor education and training in the correct method of search, collection, and preservation. But this area of forensic evidence is of great importance when material is collected and preserved in the proper way.

Footwear evidence can uncover the type of shoe, the manufacturer, even the approximate or, in some cases, precise size. If collected in the proper manner, footwear evidence can help figure out the number of suspects, their route, their participation, and the incidents that occurred during the crime.

DESIGN ELEMENTS

Manufacturers generally place a tread design on the bottom of tires and shoes, predominantly for grip and traction. All tires and shoes of the same type carry the same manufacturer's design. Each component of the design is called an "element." Contact with the ground or other sorts of damage can result in subtle changes in the tire or shoe. Obviously that damage is specific to the tire or shoe in question. In spite of the fact that all tires and shoes of the same sort begin life looking alike, because of damage and wear things will inevitably be altered.

BERTILLON'S MUG SHOT

IN HUMANS, EARMARK IDENTIFICATION IS ACHIEVED THROUGH THE EXAMINATION OF THE VISIBLE PART OF THE OUTER EAR—THE EXTERNAL PINNA. THE EAR, OVER THE YEARS NOW PROVEN TO BE UNIQUE, IS A VALUABLE IDENTIFICATION TOOL. DURING THE LATE NINETEENTH CENTURY ALPHONSE BERTILLON INTRODUCES THE "MUG SHOT" AND BECAUSE THIS RECORDS FACIAL CHARACTERISTICS AND PECULIARITIES, PARTICULARLY WITH REGARD TO THE FORMATION OF THE OUTER EAR, IT HAS BEEN INSTRUMENTAL IN THE ARREST OF MANY A CRIMINAL SUSPECT. SPECIALISTS ADVISE OF EIGHTEEN POINTS OF CHARACTERIZATION THAT CAN QUALIFY FOR PERSONAL IDENTIFICATION.

ALWAYS TOE THE LINE

There is a break-in at a Lanarkshire, Scotland, bakery in 1952. Arriving at the scene police find a safe lying on its side with the door ajar and the smell of explosives in the air. The floor is covered in a layer of flour and tracks made by footwear and bare feet prints can be seen. On the safe there are two impressions of a left sole with faint ridge detail on the big toe—photographs are taken.

A month later William Gourley is arrested and his foot and toe prints compared to those on the safe. Twenty-two identical characteristics are found. This is the first occasion when the guilt of the accused is established in the evidence of a toe print alone.

THE CHIEF FINGERPRINT OFFICER

Police are building up what is thought to be the world's biggest computer database of ear prints. The detective in charge of the new venture is John Kennerley, Chief Fingerprint Officer with the Lancashire, UK, police force.

Mr Kennerley is quoted as saying, "It's never going to be like fingerprints or DNA, but it's another tool in the forensic tool box."

If the quest to obtain ear prints becomes as commonplace as Mr Kennerley predicts, burglars who are careful to wear gloves while laying waste to someone else's property will be, as some bright spark quips, "adding ear muffs to their list of essential kit!"

EMBRACED AND FROWNED UPON

Ear print identification has been responsible for at least three other successful convictions and in England the courts find such kind of forensic evidence admissible. In the U.S. and mainland Europe it is still disapproved of, though there are those who hold out hope that this negative opinion of this form of identification will ultimately be reversed.

IT STARTED WITH A KISS

The use of finger- and palm prints is a well known aid to the trained investigator; however, prints from other parts of the body can also yield just as impressive results. The lips, or more precisely lipstick smears, can produce a print as clear as a fingerprint. Traditional lipstick provides the best results, as newer forms of "long-lasting" lipstick can lead to prints which—although very much there—are invisible to the naked eye.

In these cases far more sensitive reagents, known as lysochromes, are required to discover both recent and older lip prints. The best known lysochromes are Sudan Black, Sudan III, and Oil Red O.

ADMISSIBLE IN ANY COURT IN THE LAND?
Thanks to the leaps and bounds made in the field,
earologists are convinced that ear prints will soon
be acceptable in every court of law. They are staunch
in their view that one day this will play its part in any
case where it is found to be present and introduced into
evidence at trial. They persevere in their attempt to prove
that ear prints, just as with fingerprints, are of a unique
design—and nature never repeats itself!

LISTENING OUT FOR AN ARREST

Dorothy Wood, an infirm, profoundly deaf ninety-four-year-old is found dead at her home in Huddersfield, England, in May 1996. She has been suffocated with a pillow.

Mark Dallagher, a twenty-five-year-old man also from the Huddersfield area, in an attempt to break into Mrs. Wood's home, places his ear to a window to listen for sounds that anyone is at home—it is his undoing, for he leaves behind an ear print on the clean glass.

During his trial the court hears evidence from international ear experts, including Cornelis Van Der Lugt from the Netherlands, claiming the ear print to be a unique match to Dallagher. Protesting his innocence, Dallagher is jailed for life at Leeds Crown Court.

LOOK, DON'T LISTEN

Listening out for sounds from within houses he is about to enter become Albert James's criminal undoing. Ear print evidence is later used to convict him in 2000 of seven burglaries he is responsible for. His ear prints are discovered on windows and doors at a number of crime scenes.

SEALED WITH A KISS

In his book Homicide Investigation, *written in 1950, LeMoyne Snyder refers to a case where a woman was hit by an automobile. The left front fender of the vehicle struck her in the face with significant force. The owner of the car denied he was responsible but a lip print extracted from the bumper, lifted and photographed, matched that of the victim, proving without question that it was she who had been struck. The owner of the car was unable to further refute the charge when confronted with this damning evidence.*

THIRSTY WORK

A burglar enters a home in Japan and heads for the safe, which he proceeds to break into. As he leaves, he notices a glass of water on the table. Perhaps owing to the tenseness of the situation, he realizes he is thirsty. But he is a relatively smart burglar and wears gloves when picking up the glass. Unfortunately for him he leaves lip prints on the rim which are successfully lifted and photographed. The police suspect list names five men but only one set of lip prints match those taken from the glass. The man confesses.

TOOL MARK IMPRESSIONS

There are three categories of tool mark impressions:

Sliding—where a tool, like a screwdriver, grazes a surface leaving parallel furrows.

Compression—where a tool surface presses into a soft material, like putty.

Cutting—a combination of the other two categories, (i.e., as with scissors). Marks left, for example, on a window frame from a pry bar can be matched to a specific pry bar.

FORENSIC LINGUISTICS

"Forensic linguistics" is the name given to a number of subdisciplines within applied linguistics, and which relates to the interface between language, the law, and crime as a means to effectively understanding and interpreting.

BE CAREFUL WHO YOU SPEAK TO

It is 1971 in the state of Wisconsin and, following a trail of blood, teeth, bone fragments, and two spent .22 caliber rifle shells, a search party looking for missing Neil Lafeve finally locates his body riddled with bullets. In addition his head has been hacked off. Potential suspects are interviewed on tape but one man resists—twenty-one-year-old Brian Hussong.

A court order is granted to wiretap his house. Over the telephone Hussong's grandmother agrees to hide his guns. She later leads detectives to the location. Ballistic experts confirm a match to the bullets in Lafeve's body. An expert in voiceprint analysis serves as a witness at Hussong's trial. But although she denies saying she would hide the guns, it is his grandmother's voice on the tapes. After listening carefully to the tapes the jury returns a guilty verdict and Hussong gets life.

PAYING LIP SERVICE

Lavelle Davis is found guilty of the murder of Patrick Ferguson in Elgin, Illinois, in February 1997. A lip print photographed from a roll of duct tape found near the crime scene is the main evidence against him—in fact it is the only physical evidence to link him to the homicide and there is considerable doubt as to the guilty verdict he receives. Davis appeals against his conviction in 1999 but it is upheld. Then in March 2006, the court reverses his conviction and the case is remanded for a new trial.

CRAIG AND BENTLEY: A TRAGIC MISINTERPRETATION

One famous example of the use of expert forensic linguistic evidence is the posthumous appeal against the conviction of Derek Bentley.

In 1952, nineteen-year-old Bentley is hanged for his role in the killing of PC Sidney Miles. But it is his sixteen-year-old accomplice, Christopher Craig, who actually fires the shot. Bentley had supposedly given the police a statement but it was not a "verbatim record of dictated monologue" as police claim but rather the result of a question and answer session.

In 1998 the case is reopened and forensic linguistic experts find a number of instances suggesting that at least part of the statement was police co-authorship. Derek Bentley's conviction for murder is overturned.

FORENSIC LINGUISTS

Forensic linguists work in various fields connected to crime —both in its solution and in exonerating people falsely accused of crime. Some of these fields include:

- Analyzing the structure of the spoken word or writing.
- Determining the dialect of the language spoken.
- Author identification—comparison of writing samples of a suspect often referred to as "forensic stylistics."
- Voice identification—sometimes called "forensic phonetics."
  The above fields of research have differing levels of reliability or acceptability.

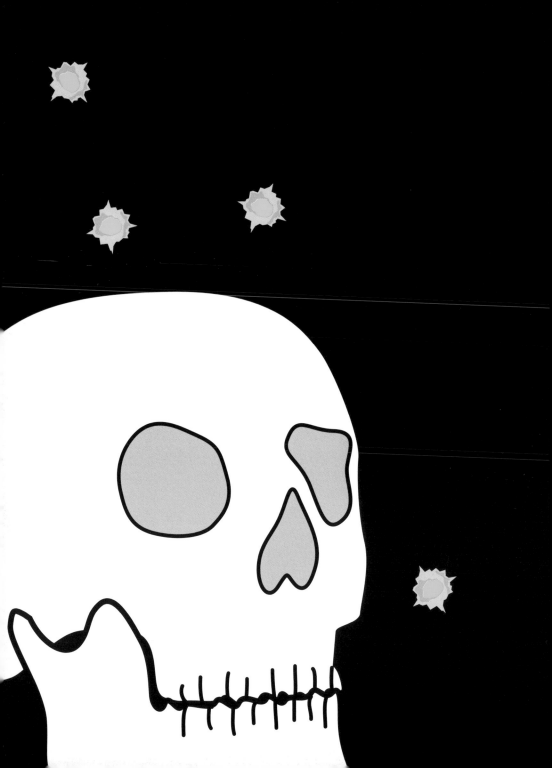

Reading Bones and Ballistics

"Bones make great witnesses, they speak softly but they never forget and they never lie . . . "
Clyde Snow, American forensic anthropologist

FORENSIC ARCHAEOLOGY

Forensic archaeology is about two things: the utilization of forensic science to examine and analyze archaeological finds and the utilization of archaeological techniques to investigate a current crime. Hence forensic archaeology is the study of human history employing scientific analysis of history's physical remains. In other words the designation "forensic archaeology" describes both the exhumation of historical remains and the investigation of modern day crimes, like the slaughter in former Yugoslavia and Rwanda.

When archaeological techniques for excavating a site are employed alongside forensic science, the results are the knowledge of people's customs and rituals, their lives and deaths. Unfortunately some mysteries of the past remain just that until new forensic archaeology can provide more convincing evidence.

OSTEO-ARCHAEOLOGISTS

Osteo-archaeologists specialize in bones. For example, they can work out whether an individual was muscular and therefore indicate whether he was involved in hard physical work. The manner in which a leg bone indicates wear and tear will demonstrate if that individual had a sedentary or active lifestyle.

A STUDY OF BONES

The data collected from the shape, marks, and texture of human bones provides the information to potentially reconstruct an individual's appearance. Signs of stress in bones can reveal an individual to be right- or left-handed. Marks left on bones can demonstrate whether the person was of slim or muscular build. Results from these tests and determination of gender, race, age, and diseases the individual may have suffered from, can permit the development of a biological profile. Match this with medical records and a victim can be identified.

NEANDERTHAL NUTRITION

WE ARE CONVINCED THAT WE MUST BE HEALTHIER TODAY THAN, SAY, NEANDERTHAL MAN, BUT THIS THEORY HAS BEEN CHALLENGED. NEANDERTHALS BECAME EXTINCT ABOUT 30,000 YEARS AGO, BUT REMAINS FOUND IN A CAVE IN CROATIA ARE DATED TO 100,000 YEARS BEFORE THAT. STUDYING THE FOSSILIZED REMAINS IN 1999, TWO AMERICAN RESEARCHERS FOUND EVIDENCE OF A BONE TUMOR IN ONE INDIVIDUAL AND SEVERAL CASES OF OSTEOARTHRITIS, BUT DESPITE STUDYING X-RAYS OF 884 BONES, INSTEAD OF INJURY AND DISEASE, THEY DISCOVERED THAT THE MAJORITY OF INDIVIDUALS WERE VERY HEALTHY ON THEIR DOUBTFUL DIETS!

SPECIALISTS

Forensic archaeology is a relatively new discipline, having been available for just the last decade. It is also new to the criminal justice system. In spite of this it has become widely accepted in the U.K. and in increasing locations in the U.S. For example, the FBI includes archaeology specialists in its field of operation.

EARLY INTERBREEDING?

In Portugal the skeleton of a four-year-old child is unearthed. Although she has limbs like a Neanderthal, her teeth and skull resemble those of modern humans. This leads some anthropologists to wonder if this is proof of interbreeding between early humans and Neanderthals. However, for the first time, fragments of DNA recently extracted from Neanderthal fossils have proved not to be similar to the genetic makeup of any modern Europeans. Also CAT scans indicate that modern man has a different inner ear structure to Neanderthals. The signs are that no interbreeding took place although advances in genetic research could still prove otherwise.

ON THE OTHER HAND

UNTIL THE MID-TWENTIETH CENTURY, LEFT-HANDED PEOPLE HAVE BEEN INDUCED TO USE THEIR RIGHT HANDS FOR TACTILE LABOR LIKE WRITING. IT IS A FACT THAT THE BONES OF THE PREDOMINANT ARM GROW LONGER AND THE MUSCLES STRONGER. THE QUESTION IS, IF SOCIETY DOES NOT ACTIVELY ENCOURAGE THE USE OF THE RIGHT HAND, WOULD MORE PEOPLE BE LEFT-HANDED?

A PROJECT CARRIED OUT IN THE 1970S BY JAMES STEEL FINDS THAT ONLY THREE PERCENT OF PEOPLE AGED 55–64 USE THEIR LEFT HAND FOR MANIPULATIVE TASKS, WHILE THE FIGURES FOR 15–24-YEAR-OLDS IS ELEVEN PERCENT.

THIS LATTER ASSESSMENT IS MADE BY USING RADIOGRAPHIC MEASUREMENTS OF THE YOUNG PEOPLE'S ARM BONES. IN YORKSHIRE, MEDIEVAL SKELETONS HAD THEIR ARM BONES MEASURED AND THE NUMBER OF LEFT-HANDED INDIVIDUALS IN THE RURAL, UNEDUCATED POPULATION WAS APPROXIMATELY THE SAME AS IN THE LATE TWENTIETH CENTURY. THE QUESTION REMAINS, IS CULTURAL PRESSURE THE CAUSE OF FEWER PEOPLE BEING LEFT-HANDED?

THE SKELETONS OF EASTER ISLAND

The mutineers from "The Bounty" land on Easter Island fourteen hundred miles from Pitcairn (the closest habitable island in the Pacific Ocean). It has long been thought that Easter Island had originally been settled by people from South America. But their crops, tools, and language were similar to South-east Asian cultures. Recently DNA analysis on twelve Easter Island skeletons has confirmed that the original inhabitants arrived around AD 400 and were definitely Polynesians.

THE LIFE AND DEATH OF THE INUIT

Eight wonderfully preserved bodies—six women, a female child, and a newly born baby girl—are discovered in a cave in Greenland in 1972. This was the site of an Inuit settlement abandoned some five hundred years previously. How did they die? Was there an epidemic? Did they die of hunger? Why were they all female?

The bodies are in a perfect state of preservation due to the bitterly cold winds that had effectively "freeze-dried" them after death. A forensic archaeologist studies the remains using CT scans, giving a three-dimensional picture of the inside of the bodies. He finds they did not starve because there is food in the women's stomachs.

They did not die of hypothermia—they were dressed appropriately for the extremely cold temperatures, the baby's clothes in particular were constructed from the skin of baby seals with the fur facing the body. So we know a little about how the Inuit lived but have yet to discover how they died.

EYMUND THE VIKING

April 1991 and Eymund the Viking is introduced to the public. In York, U.K., once a Viking stronghold, the Jorvik Viking Centre project involves the 1986 discovery of the Fishergate cemetery excavations in which more than sixty-eight burials are found. Examined is the corpse of a man standing five foot six inches tall. His skull is laser-scanned by the collaborative efforts of the York Archaeological Trust and the Medical Physics Department of University College Hospital, London.

Plaster of Paris is used to repair damage to the ancient skull. Computer images are produced after comparisons are made with that of a male of approximately the same build. Likenesses in facial tissue structure are made in an effort to see what the Viking they call Eymund would have looked like in life.

SCIENTISTS, EXAMINING A MALE SKELETON FOUND IN 1923 AT STONEHENGE, DISCOVER THAT PREVIOUS STUDIES DETERMINING THE MAN HAD DIED FROM NATURAL CAUSES ARE IN FACT WRONG. HE HAD BEEN BEHEADED. IN ARRIVING AT THIS CONCLUSION SCIENTISTS HAD EMPLOYED VARIOUS DISCIPLINES, I.E., CARBON DATING, BONE STUDIES, ANALYSES OF THE SKELETON'S DAMAGED VERTEBRAE AND THE ANGLE OF THE WOUND, FACIAL RECONSTRUCTION, AND COMPARISON WITH OTHER HUMAN REMAINS. THE THEORIES CONCERNING HIS MURDER ABOUND. WAS HE A RITUAL SACRIFICE? WAS HE A THIEF? WAS HE A PAGAN IN A NEWLY ESTABLISHED CHRISTIAN COMMUNITY? THE MYSTERIES OF STONEHENGE PERSEVERE DESPITE THE ADVANCES IN FORENSIC TECHNOLOGY.

MODERN TECHNOLOGY IN ANCIENT EGYPT

Modern scientific techniques are now being employed in the study of ancient Egypt. Remote sensing technologies enable archaeologists to locate tombs, buildings and buried artifacts. Cutting-edge diagnostic techniques such as tissue biopsies, endoscopy, CT-scans and X-rays provide a powerful insight into the diseases that beset these ancient people. Complex chemical analyses make it possible for Egyptologists to study their diet and how recreational drugs were a part of life.

IN THE GROUNDS OF GRANTS HILL HOUSE

The world remembers that in 1974 Lord Lucan went missing from his London home under suspicious circumstances, never to be seen again. He is suspected of having murdered his children's nanny and attempting to kill his wife. But what became of him?

An individual comes forward claiming to have witnessed Lucan's murder. He maintains the body was thrown into a cesspit in the grounds of Grants Hill House. Investigators using building plans discover a cesspit did exist on the site of the since-demolished house. But does it conceal the Earl's body?

Over the last decade technology has advanced spectacularly, with much progress in sounding equipment and underground X-rays, and forensic archaeologist Lucy Sideburn, a specialist in the recovery of human remains, is convinced there is a reason to investigate further because she has evidence of ground disturbance at the site. But the world will have to wait for more information. At present it is only the gardener who is permitted to do any digging.

FORENSIC ANTHROPOLOGY

Positive identification in anthropology is the ultimate objective of forensic science. Its achievement is assured when a set of skeletal remains matches a set of biological characteristics of a person. In order to establish this identification, the investigator involved will require that the skeletal remains relate to DNA analysis, such as dental or medical records or specific antemortem injuries.

LOCATING THE TRAUMA

When searching for evidence of trauma or injury, it is important that a set of skeletal remains has been cleansed of any debris. Sometimes any organs or other soft tissues will have completely disintegrated, so only the bones remain to yield clues as to how a victim may have died. Bullet trauma can often result in smashed or fragmented bones, whereas scrapes and similar penetrative markings will point toward stab wounds. If a victim has sustained heavy trauma from a blow, or blows, from a blunt object, this will leave damage to the bones, which will often be broken.

PHRENOLOGY: BY DR. GALL

Viennese physician Dr. Franz Joseph Gall comes up with the theory of phrenology in 1796. At the time it is heralded for the revolutionary discovery that it is. In theorizing that, as a person thinks, the shape of his or her brain is affected, thus influencing the bone structure of the cranium and resulting in irregular surface structures such as bumps and nodules, Gall concludes that a criminally minded individual may be more easily identified; such "bumps" or as phrenologists refer to them "faculties" are said to be responsible for dictating antisocial development. It is a highly contested theory, especially in modern day forensics where it is somewhat frowned upon and branded archaic and misleading.

GENDER DIFFERENCES

When a body has decayed to such an extent that only bones remain, naturally the process of identification becomes far more difficult. It is however still relatively simple to identify some of the basics, such as gender and approximate age. Males tend to have a larger superorbital crest above the eye socket and a more pronounced nuchal crest at the base of the skull. The differences in the structure of the bones, in particular the pubic shape, subpubic angle and the presence of the ventral arc are perhaps the best areas for assessment.

AGE DIFFERENCES

Accurate estimates of age can always be determined from the fusion of growth chambers in children or from the condition of the bones joined at the pubic symphysis or from the rib ends of adults. In the case of children, however, the best indicator of approximate age is in the detailed changes to the teeth that have occurred as the child develops and ages.

ETHNIC DIFFERENCES

Human remains, even when skeletal or in a state of decay, can provide examiners with an idea of ethnic origins. The skull shape, and in particular the jaw, can identify the race of a victim. Those of Far Eastern descent have triple-mounted molars contained within a wide jaw, whereas those of European ancestry tend to have teeth set very close together in a narrower jaw structure. More accurate results can be obtained, once the victim's racial group and gender is known, from the Forensic Anthropological Data Bank, housed at the University of Tennessee, by using a program called Fordisc 2.0.

SIZE OF THE BODY

It should come as no surprise to learn that you do not need the full skeleton when attempting to establish the size of a body—even when the victim has been dismembered, the height of the body can still be ascertained. One technique that is accurate to within a few inches is to measure the length of the femur or tibia and apply the scale to the remainder of the body. The program called Fordisc 2.0 can achieve more accurate results once the victim's racial group and gender is known.

LOS DESAPARECIDOS

BETWEEN 1976 AND 1983 ARGENTINA'S MILITARY REGIME IS RESPONSIBLE FOR THE ABDUCTION, RAPE, TORTURE, AND MURDER OF NEARLY TWENTY THOUSAND MEN, WOMEN, AND CHILDREN. THESE BECOME KNOWN AS "THE DISAPPEARED" (*LOS DESAPARECIDOS*). IN 1984 FORENSIC ANTHROPOLOGIST CLYDE SNOW LEADS A PARTY OF VOLUNTEER ARGENTINEAN STUDENTS IN THE SEARCH AND EXCAVATION OF HUNDREDS OF MASS GRAVES. THIS METICULOUS STUDY LEADS TO THE CREATION OF THE ARGENTINE FORENSIC ANTHROPOLOGY TEAM, AN ORGANIZATION INTENT UPON EMPLOYING FORENSIC SCIENCE IN THE INVESTIGATION OF HUMAN RIGHTS VIOLATIONS.

THE SKELETON THAT LIMPED

IN 1899 A SKELETON YIELDS ENOUGH SECRETS TO LEAD POLICE TO THE DOOR OF A PAIR OF KILLERS.

BY THE SIDE OF A RIVER NEAR LYONS, FRANCE, A MALE CORPSE IN AN ADVANCED STAGE OF DECOMPOSITION IS DISCOVERED. NEARBY RESTS A WOODEN TRUNK WHICH SEEMS TO HAVE BEEN SENT VIA RAIL TO LYONS FROM PARIS. A POSTMORTEM EXAMINATION IS CARRIED OUT BY ALEXANDRE LACASSAGNE, PROFESSOR OF FORENSIC MEDICINE AT LYONS UNIVERSITY. FOCUSING ON THE CONDITION OF THE RIGHT LEG AND ANKLE OF THE SKELETON HE NOTES THAT THE MUSCLES OF THIS LIMB ARE WEAKER THAN THOSE OF THE OTHER. HE DETERMINES THAT THE OWNER SUFFERED TUBERCULAR DISEASE IN THIS LEG, CORRECTLY DEDUCING THAT IN LIFE HE WOULD HAVE WALKED WITH A PRONOUNCED LIMP. INQUIRIES REVEAL THAT A MISSING BAILIFF HAD BEEN TREATED FOR A KNEE COMPLAINT AND DID WALK WITH A LIMP. THANKS TO THE PROFESSOR'S ENDEAVORS THE DEAD MAN'S MISTRESS AND HER LOVER ARE ULTIMATELY CONVICTED OF MURDERING HIM.

JOHN WAYNE GACY: RECONSTRUCTING A FIEND'S VICTIMS

In December 1978 serial murderer John Wayne Gacy is arrested in connection with the disappearance of a missing sixteen-year-old boy. He will be charged with—and later convicted of—the murders of thirty-three young men, making him the most prolific mass killer—in terms of the most murder convictions—in United States history, and guaranteeing him a place in the *Guinness Book of World Records*.

Identification of the remains of Gacy's victims proves difficult. Investigators can account for only half the bodies and seek out bone specialists—forensic anthropologists.

The remains are examined for unusual osteological features and a sculptress is asked to examine the skulls. With her vast knowledge of facial anatomy she applies modelling clay to the victim's skulls in order to accentuate features such as the mouth and cheeks. She also reconstructs noses from any slivers of bone remaining. The case is singular in highlighting the contribution that can be made by forensic anthropologists.

A LOT OF UNCERTAINTY:
THE BALLAD OF HENRY LEE LUCAS

Another infamous serial killer named Henry Lee Lucas is arrested in June 1983, initially on a firearms violation. He is subsequently charged with killing eighty-two-year-old Kate Rich and her twelve-year-old niece, Becky Powell.

The forensic evidence in the Powell and Rich cases will later be criticized as being inconclusive. A single bone fragment recovered from a wood-burning stove is said to be Kate Rich's, and a skeleton roughly matches Becky Powell's age and size. The medical examiner could not however positively identify either set of remains. Although Lucas confesses to both murders he is already known to be a sociopathic liar, having taken responsibility for dozens of other unsolved homicides—most of which are easily proven not to have been committed by him.

IN A LABORATORY AT THE UNIVERSITY OF TENNESSEE, A SHORT DISTANCE FROM WHAT IS KNOWN AS THE "BODY FARM," A HUGE COLLECTION OF DONATED HUMAN SKELETONS ARE HOUSED. THERE ARE ABOUT FIVE HUNDRED SAMPLES WITH MORE BEING ADDED EVERY YEAR. IT IS HERE THAT THE BONES ARE CHEMICALLY ANALYZED AND PROVIDE INFORMATION ON, FOR INSTANCE, THE AGE OF A PERSON WHEN THEY DIED. DETAILS GLEANED FROM THESE BONES CAN BE QUITE SPECIFIC, EVEN INCLUDING WHAT THE PERSON ATE IN LIFE.

BUCK RUXTON TRIES TO GET AWAY WITH MURDER

On September 15, 1935, Dr. Buck Ruxton murders his wife, Isabella, and his nursemaid, Mary Jane Rogerson, at the family home in Lancaster, U.K. The bodies are dismembered and dumped over the border, in Scotland. Due to decomposition police are unable to identify the jumbled set of remains so a photograph of Mrs Ruxton is later superimposed onto one of the skulls and is found to match perfectly. Ruxton, following the double homicide, foolishly invites one of his patients to help clean his home (the patient notices a number of bloodstains in the property) and is later arrested. He is hanged at Strangeways Prison on May 12, 1936.

DETERMINING SEX—THE SKULL

METHODS EMPLOYED TO ESTIMATE HEIGHT AND AGE ARE DIFFERENT FOR MALES AND FEMALES AND BECAUSE OF THIS THE SEX OF A SET OF HUMAN REMAINS NEEDS TO BE ESTABLISHED AT THE OUTSET. FOR A LONG TIME, THE SKULL WAS TRADITIONALLY EXAMINED FIRST AND THIS WAS THE SOLE METHOD OF DETERMINING A PERSON'S SEX. THE SKULL IS STILL EXAMINED BUT IS NOW CONSIDERED AS A CORRELATIVE INDICATION ONLY.

NOWADAYS FORENSIC ANTHROPOLOGISTS CHOOSE TO USE THE PUBIC BONES INSTEAD DUE TO THEIR MORE OBVIOUS FEATURES. HENCE THE MOST IMPORTANT BONE IS THE "INNOMINATE" BONE WHICH CONTAINS THE PELVIS, THE SECOND BONE OF CHOICE FOR EXAMINATION BEING THE FEMUR OR HUMERUS.

TED BUNDY AND THE BITE MARK
THAT SEALED HIS FATE

On January 15, 1978, Lisa Levy is raped and murdered. Among other injuries there is an unusual bite mark on her left buttock, which is photographed by police.

America's number one serial killer Theodore Robert "Ted" Bundy is under suspicion of leaving it, and investigators request a dental impression for comparison with the bite mark.

Forensic odontologist Dr. Richard Souviron takes photographs of Bundy's teeth and gums. While the jury look at these, Dr. Souviron explains how the photographs of the victim's bite match the dental impressions of Bundy's teeth.

He is able to demonstrate their unique size, shape and alignment. Bundy is found guilty—the first time in Florida's history that a bite mark is accepted as evidence.

TUBE OF LIFE AND DEATH

In November 1991, sixty-five-year-old Thelma Younkin is strangled, bitten, and raped in her room at the Post Park Motel. The oxygen tube that Thelma Younkin uses to help her breathe is used to choke her to death by her killer.

A fellow resident at the motel, Bobby Lee Tankersley, is convicted of her murder and sent to Arizona's Death Row. He is convicted mainly due to testimony given by a forensic dentist who said the bite mark on Younkin's body matched Tankersley's teeth. It is enough to convince the jury.

THE SNAGGLETOOTH KILLER

Former postal worker Ray Krone is sentenced to death in 1992. He is an innocent man. Dr. Raymond Rawson's trial testimony was the lynchpin of the prosecution's case, and saw him placed on Arizona's Death Row. Rawson testified that bite marks found on a slain Phoenix cocktail waitress matched Krone's teeth.

At Krone's 1996 retrial Rawson is present again, reinforcing his claim that Krone's teeth had made the bite marks. Rawson says that a pattern of blood found on the victim's bra is "a scientific match."

Krone spends over a decade in prison. Then DNA testing proves Rawson wrong, links another man to the killing and exonerates Krone. "The snaggletooth killer," as Krone has been dubbed recently, appears on the ABC television show "Extreme Makeover," where his teeth are reexamined slightly more publicly.

A PIECE OF CHEESE

ARTHUR HUTCHINSON IS CONVICTED OF THE OCTOBER 24, 1983 MURDER, RAPE, AND AGGRAVATED BURGLARY OF THE LAITNER FAMILY. SEVERAL PIECES OF CLASS EVIDENCE SUCH AS BLOODSTAINS AND SHOE PRINTS SEAL HIS FATE. THERE IS ALSO A DENTAL IMPRESSION LEFT IN A PIECE OF CHEESE DISCOVERED AT THE SCENE OF THE CRIME. FORENSIC EXAMINERS ARE ABLE TO CONFIDENTLY ESTABLISH THAT THE IMPRESSION HAD BEEN MADE BY THE ACCUSED. WITH SUCH STRONG AND DAMNING FORENSIC EVIDENCE TYING HIM TO THE CRIME, HUTCHINSON IS LEFT WITH LITTLE HOPE OF CONTESTING THESE CHARGES.

WHICH TWIN BIT?

TWO TWINS HAD ENGAGED IN CONSENSUAL "ROUGH" SEX WITH A MALE SEVERAL MONTHS PREVIOUSLY DURING WHICH ONE OF THE TWINS BIT THE MALE'S BUTTOCK. ONE SISTER HAD HIV—FOR WHICH THE MALE PARTICIPANT NOW ALSO TESTED POSITIVE. THE QUESTION FOR FORENSIC ODONTOLOGIST PERCY MICHAELS WAS WHICH SISTER BIT THE MAN, AND HAD SHE COMMITTED A CRIME BY SO DOING?

PHOTOGRAPHING THE BITE MARK USING FILM SENSITIVE TO ULTRAVIOLET LIGHT—THE FAR END OF THE BLUE SPECTRUM OF LIGHT CAN REVEAL UNDERLYING TISSUE DAMAGE MONTHS LATER—DR. MICHAELS NEXT COMPARES THE IMAGE WITH X-RAYS OF EACH TWIN'S TEETH.

DESPITE THE TWINS BEING IDENTICAL SEVEN POINTS OF DIFFERENCE ARE FOUND BY DR. MICHAELS. STUDYING BOTH SETS OF DENTITION HE IS ABLE TO CONCLUDE THAT THE HIV POSITIVE SISTER WAS NOT THE TWIN RESPONSIBLE FOR BITING THE MAN.

GORDON HAY'S JAGGED TOOTH

In a pivotal case of subsequent bite mark analysis, on August 7, 1967, in a small town between Edinburgh and Glasgow in Scotland, Gordon Hay batters and strangles a fifteen-year-old girl named Linda Peacock. Investigators believe an attempt at rape has been made by the killer. A deep bruise appearing on the dead girl's breast is found to be a bite mark. Hay is later rounded up and a jagged tooth he possesses is an identical match for part of the mark found on Linda Peacock's breast.

WHEN BITING HAPPENS

Teeth are commonly used in the struggle between a victim and their attacker. Often it is the only resource left available to the victim. The assailant, particularly in sexual attacks such as rape and child sexual abuse and sexual homicide, will bite the victim as a demonstration of his dominance and fury in an animalistic fashion.

Human bite marks can be found on nearly any area of the body. If the assailant is bitten it is often on the hands and arms. Bites on male victims are usually on the shoulders and arms, Whilst female victims are commonly bitten on the legs and breasts.

THE TWO DOCTORS AND THE DENTURES

Dr. John Webster and Dr. George Parkman are both doctors at Harvard Medical School in 1849. Dr. Parkman lends Dr. Webster a substantial amount of money. After a series of excuses that prevent Webster from repaying the loan, Parkman visits him to retrieve the sum. Parkman is never seen alive again.

The college janitor becomes suspicious of Webster after finding his usually accessible laboratory is locked. When he confronts Webster, the doctor tries to bribe him with a large Thanksgiving turkey. Later that night, the janitor makes a hole in the laboratory wall and discovers two human legs and a pelvis. The police find numerous body parts and a set of dentures in the furnace. Parkman's dentist kept a cast of his dentures and the two match. Webster is sentenced to death.

CLAUDIUS, NERO, AND SOME VICTIMS

AD 45–70, Rome, and Emperor Claudius and his son Nero have two variants on the theme of dental identification associated with them. Nero's mistress Sabina is alleged to have persuaded him to murder his mother, Agrippina. Her body is subsequently identified after the examination of the skull, where two maxillary canine teeth are matched. Sabina is also said to have persuaded Nero to murder his wife, who is believed to have been identified by a malocclusion or discolored tooth.

CHARLES "THE BOLD"

The year is 1477, France, and the corpse of Charles "The Bold," Duke of Burgundy, is identified after a thorough dental examination. His jaw is found to have an absence of certain anterior teeth. It is learned that the duke has been dispatched by the Swiss in Nancy and from examining the unique set of dentures in the mangled remains it is able to be substantiated that the dead man and the duke are one and the same.

WILLIAM THE CONQUEROR'S MALOCCLUSION

IT IS IN ENGLAND THAT THE GREAT BATTLE OF HASTINGS TAKES PLACE IN THE YEAR 1066. LEGEND HAS IT THAT WILLIAM THE CONQUEROR HAS BITTEN INTO A SEAL OF WAX. KING WILLIAM THE FIRST (HIS OFFICIAL TITLE) HAS AN UNUSUAL MALOCCLUSION ALIGNMENT AND IT IS THIS THAT HELPS IN IDENTIFYING THE IMPRESSION IN THE SEAL AS BELONGING TO THE REVERED KING AND GREAT BATTLER OF HASTINGS HIMSELF.

"MRS. MCALLISTER'S" TEETH

In 1813 in Scotland, a dead lady known as "Mrs. McAllister" has her corpse "snatched" from her grave, it is soon suspected for the purposes of dissection for profit and/or illegal medical purposes. At the later trial of those accused of grave-robbing, a denture is produced, at first thought to fit within the toothless maxilla of the body. It is later deduced that the denture does not articulate properly with the remaining tooth structure. It is guessed that some shady substitution of corpses has been underway, but this is not conclusively proven.

THE FIRE OF BAZAR DE LA CHARITÉ

Paris, France, 1897, and the noted tragedy that is the fire at the Bazar de la Charité ball consumes many lives. Identification of the numerous charred remains is possible after accessing suspected victims' dental records. Dr. Amoedo and two colleagues with extensive experience in the field of dentistry manage to successfully identify most of the twenty-six dead. The grisly yet surprisingly large tally of identifications made by the trio is heralded as a remarkable success.

In 1973 the world screams as twenty-seven corpses of young men and boys are discovered buried under a disused boatshed and along a nearby beach in the Houston, Texas, area. Sadistic serial murderer Dean Corll is already dead, killed by a hail of bullets fired into him by a young accomplice, Elmer Wayne Henley.

Identifying the body of the killer is not a problem, as police are called shortly after Corll is executed. Identifying the sad remains of his many victims is another matter. When unearthed from their makeshift graves most bodies are in advanced states of decomposition. Extensive forensic dentistry skills are utilized in identifying the dead.

BATTLE OF THE DENTISTS

Also in 1973 two leading U.S. forensic odontologists named Dr. Lowell Levine (New York) and Lester Luntz (Connecticut) offer opposing dental evidence in a typically heinous murder case where in addition to being raped, the victim's thigh has been bitten by the killer. This piece of dental evidence is enough to convict vicious sexual predator Richard Malone.

"JIM JONESTOWN"

IN 1979, NINE HUNDRED AND THIRTEEN DEAD BODIES NEED IDENTIFYING AT THE PEOPLE'S TEMPLE FULL GOSPEL CHURCH AT JONESTOWN IN GUYANA. ALL OF THE DECEASED, IT IS LEARNED, HAVE PARTICIPATED IN A MASS SUICIDE WHICH BORDERS ON MURDER, MASTERMINDED AS IT WAS BY JAMES WARREN JONES, A MANIACAL CULT LEADER, GUARANTEED IMMORTAL INFAMY AS A RESULT OF THE DIABOLICAL INSTRUCTIONS IMPOSED UPON HIS MANY BRAINWASHED DISCIPLES. MANY LONG HOURS ARE SPENT COMPARING DENTAL RECORDS AND FINDING MATCH AFTER MATCH.

JUST TO MAKE SURE

In 1981 the deceased Lee Harvey Oswald, alleged slayer of President John F. Kennedy, is exhumed. The purpose of the exercise is to ascertain whether the notorious reputed assassin Oswald is indeed the corpse that lies buried. This is prompted following widespread rumors that a Soviet spy had been impersonating Oswald and may in fact be the deceased person buried in the grave marked Oswald.

Dr. James A. Cottone, an eminent U.S. forensic dentist, using Oswald's military dental record, makes a positive identification of the remains.

LAKE AND NG'S CABIN OF DEATH

Fragments of teeth and dental charts enable forensic experts to identify the remains of two young women in Calaveras County, California in 1985. Their murders had been video-taped and the grim evidence is found at a remote cabin in Wilseyville which belonged to the now deceased Leonard Lake, who had swallowed a cyanide capsule shortly after being taken into police custody.

Detectives have been investigating the discovery of some eleven bodies found buried in trenches around the cabin. The victims had all been kidnapped, tortured, raped, and murdered.

Arrested, Lake manages to swallow his death pill but his murder companion, Charles Chitat Ng, will not escape justice and is later found guilty of the murders of three women, six men, and two baby boys.

IDENTIFYING A FRIEND

In the mid-1770s, a U.S. coppersmith, silversmith, and engraver named Paul Revere creates a pair of dentures, bound together with silver wire and supported by a bridge fashioned from a hippopotamus's tusk. Revere is later able to identify the body of his friend, Dr. John Warren, who had been shot in the head by British forces in the battle at Bunker Hill north of Boston.

FRED AND ROSE WEST

Scientists, studying the teeth of one of the serial killer couple's victims, pronounce her to be a young girl whose two front teeth had been temporarily crowned. They instruct investigating officers to look for a young girl of a particular age who had gone missing in the time between receiving temporary and permanent crowns. They speculate that the damage could have been caused by a sports injury.

A local police officer says that when she was at school, playing in a hockey match, one of the girls had had an accident to her front teeth. The murder team decide to follow this up and amazingly discover that the injured hockey player was indeed the victim.

NATURAL TEETH

Dental records can be priceless when identifying a body. Teeth last longer than other physical elements after death and they also differ dramatically in detail from person to person. Even taking into account small changes in the condition of teeth over a time span of many years, records are often accurate enough to provide a positive identification.

DENTURES

EVEN IF NATURAL TEETH HAVE BEEN REPLACED BY DENTURES, THESE TOO CAN POSITIVELY IDENTIFY THE OWNER. IN THE U.S., DENTURES ARE OFTEN MARKED WITH NOT ONLY THE WEARER'S NAME BUT ALSO HIS OR HER SOCIAL SECURITY NUMBER.

SALIVA EXCESS

Substantial amounts of saliva are left behind at crime scenes through licking, sucking, and biting. This saliva is easily retrieved and sent for DNA analysis. Commonly, cotton swabs are used to obtain samples. Adequate amounts of salivary evidence are captured by the use of multiple swabs, particularly when a procedure called the "double swab" technique is used. This involves a moist swab followed by a dry swab. Under perfect conditions the limit of time for obtaining salivary DNA is about sixty hours after deposit.

SAWN OFF?

The way in which pellets disperse fired from a shot gun varies greatly depending on the length of the barrel, or the "choke" as it is sometimes known. If the barrel is sawn off, i.e., made shorter, the gun when fired at close range can cause very large wounds as the pellets spread further at speed, but it is very unreliable at distance, again due to the spreading. A longer choke is more reliable at distance as the pellets stay closely grouped for longer before separating.

ZEROING IN ON SPECIFICS

Firearm specialists are able to compare and match bullets to a specific weapon. They are equipped to detect gunshot residue from the clothing or skin of a suspect and are able to accurately estimate the distance from the fired gun to the designated target. Of course, it is also important to trace the serial number of the weapon to the registered owner. Some shooters, in a deliberate effort to avoid detection, will attempt to file the number off to prevent this happening; however, very often a serial number is recoverable.

SACCO AND VANZETTI

Years after the murder of a paymaster and security guard the Sacco–Vanzetti case was still topical. Due to worldwide protest the execution date had been postponed several times as there was doubt as to whether Nicola Sacco's gun had been the murder weapon.

By 1927 firearms identification is on the verge of becoming a recognized forensic science and Dr. Calvin Goddard is studying the photographs taken in 1923 of the Sacco–Vanzetti bullets. His comparison microscope reveals beyond any doubt that the fatal bullet had been fired from Sacco's gun. On the strength of his findings the Governor refuses to commute the sentences and Nicola Sacco and Bartolomeo Vanzetti go to the electric chair.

MARK DAVID CHAPMAN: DID HE DO IT?

Twenty-four years after the shooting of John Lennon, growing evidence would appear to indicate that Mark Chapman is innocent even though he confessed to the crime. The mounting evidence appears to demonstrate that Chapman could not have shot Lennon because, according to the autopsy report, all four entry wounds were on the wrong side of the body for the location in which Chapman was standing at the time.

Photos taken at the time show that Chapman stood to the right and behind Lennon. The real killer would probably have been positioned behind Lennon and to his left.

A FATHER'S SINS

John Dale Cavaness had lost two sons—both allegedly committing suicide—Mark some time before Sean. At a party, only hours after Sean's death, Cavaness is the life and soul—peculiar behaviour one might think for a man who would subsequently tell police he had witnessed his son's suicide; appropriate behaviour though for a ruthless murderer who had killed two of his children.

Sean had been shot twice in the back of the head. One shot had been fired from less than one inch away but was not a contact wound because of the gunpowder stippling to the skin. The second shot was fired from a distance of twelve to eighteen inches as he lay on the ground. Police are already suspicious of Cavaness's involvement in Mark's death and he is charged with murder. He later hangs himself in his cell on Death Row.

THE FIRST BULLET TRACE

In 1835, policeman Henry Goddard becomes the first man to trace a bullet to the specific gun that fired it. Before mass manufacture, gun owners molded their own bullets. Investigating a robbery in Southampton where the butler had been shot at by the burglars, Goddard finds the bullet buried in the butler's bed headboard. Inspecting the butler's own pistol and bullet mold, he discovers a defect in the mold that matches the bullet exactly. The butler confesses to the robbery and admits firing the shot as part of a cover story to divert suspicion from himself.

A GUN IS A GUN?

In mass-produced guns, each type is as individual as a fingerprint. The barrel's caliber, the number of grooves in its rifling, and the direction of the grooves' spiral from the breach to the muzzle always share the same standardized characteristics, although each brand of gun differs in these characteristics. For example, Browning and Colt both have six grooves in the rifling, but those in the Browning turn clockwise, whereas in the Colt they turn counter-clockwise. These differences are invaluable to forensic examiners when attempting to match the make and class of a gun to bullets found at a crime scene.

BRUCE RAGSDALE EXPERIMENTS

IN THE 1980S PATHOLOGIST BRUCE RAGSDALE PERFORMS EXPERIMENTS TO DEMONSTRATE THE EFFECTS OF DIFFERENT SORTS OF GUNSHOTS ON HUMAN TISSUE AND BONE. HE ENCASES LEG BONES FROM CORPSES IN BLOCKS OF TRANSPARENT GELATIN, THEN FIRES DIFFERENT SORTS OF GUNS INTO THEM. SLOW MOTION IS USED TO FILM EACH EXPERIMENT, THUS ENABLING THE TRAJECTORY OF THE BULLET, THE SHATTERING OF BONE, AND THE SHOCK WAVES TO BE ANALYZED IN DETAIL.

THE MURDER OF PC GUTTERIDGE

On Tuesday 27 September, 1927, in a southern English town, the body of PC George Gutteridge is found. He has been shot four times in the face. Police later recover from a bloodstained car a cartridge case marked RLIV. This marking indicates that it is an old Mark IV type made at the Royal Laboratory in Woolwich Arsenal for troops in World War I.

The case has been scarred by a fault in the breech block of the gun which had fired it. The foremost gun expert of the day, Mr. Robert Churchill, determines that the bullet had been fired by a Webley revolver. Mr. Churchill examines the suspects' weapon and finds it to be the same one which had caused the distinctive mark on the cartridge case. The Sunday Dispatch newspaper carries the headline "Hanged by a microscope," reflecting the fact that microscopic examination of the cartridge cases had provided the crucial evidence to convict Guy Fredrick Browne and Patrick Kennedy of murder.

THIS IS NOT AN EXIT!

In most shootings, the entry wound is smooth and circular as the bullet tears through the body's tissues. However when the bullet re-emerges from the body it often causes a far larger and irregular shaped "exit wound." This is most often caused by the bullet smashing through bone or thick muscle, dramatically changing the bullet's angle of trajectory. There are also usually no abrasion marks around the skin at the exit point, which are characteristic of an entry wound.

UP CLOSE AND PERSONAL

The bullet and its damage are not the only helpful evidence to be found when someone is shot at close range. If the shot is within a range of twelve to eighteen inches, examiners can expect to find soot around the bullet wound. At around twenty-five to thirty-six inches scattered traces of partially burned gunpowder will be found around the general area of the wound. At greater distances, a dark ring around the entry wound made up of lead, carbon, oil, and dirt is removed from the bullet and left on the surface of the body. This is known as a "bullet wipe."

A SHOT IN THE DARK

SHOTGUN WOUNDS ARE DIFFERENT TO HANDGUN OR RIFLE WOUNDS. THE SHOTGUN FIRES A COLLECTION OF SMALL PELLETS WHICH SPREAD OUT OVER DISTANCE. AT VERY CLOSE RANGE, THE PELLETS HAVE NO TIME TO SPREAD SO THEY TEND TO ENTER THE SAME SPOT TOGETHER, CAUSING HORRIFIC DAMAGE. AT SHORT RANGE IT ALSO LEAVES A "TATTOO" OF LOCALIZED SCORCHING AROUND THE ENTRY WOUND. AT DISTANCES OF OVER FOUR FEET, THE SEVERITY OF THE WOUND DECREASES AS THE PELLETS SEPARATE FURTHER FROM EACH OTHER, LEAVING NONE OF THE SCORCHING MARKS CHARACTERISTIC OF A CLOSE-UP SHOT.

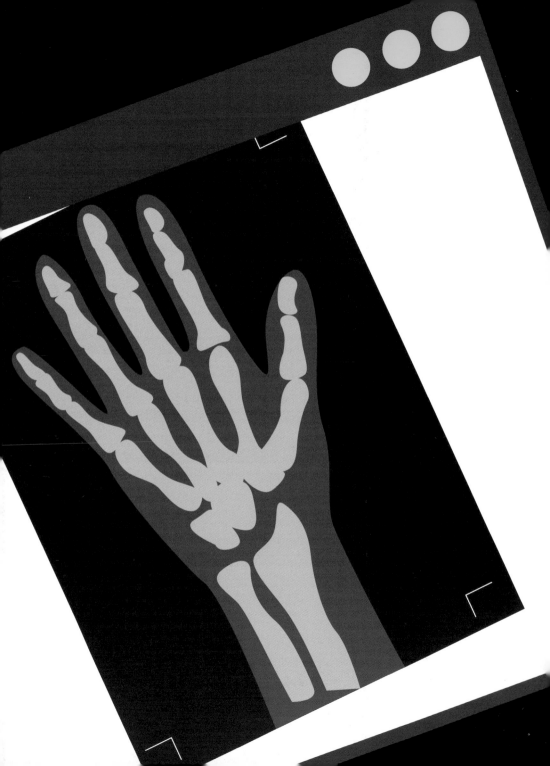

Death's Visitors

"Dead men do tell tales."
Meghan A.T.B. Reese

The study of insects and other arthropods in accordance with legal issues is a science called forensic entomology. Its three subfields are: urban, stored-product, and medicolegal.

Medicolegal forensic entomology includes arthropod presence in various crimes such as murder, rape, and other such serious sexual or violent assaults, and also drug and other such contraband trafficking. Forensic entomology also encompasses cases of suicide.

MURDER BUGS

In the course of a murder investigation forensic entomology explores what type of insect laid a particular egg within a corpse. The process aids in ascertaining the time of death at postmortem interval (PMI) and location of the homicide at hand.

There are certain necrophagous (corpse-eating) types of insect, one such being the fly, which favors a moist corpse. Maggots also feed upon a corpse and the flesh is easier for them to chew. Larval flies are used by forensic entomologists to gauge the postmortem interval, since eggs and larvae on the body may have been consumed prior to the arrival at the scene of investigators.

LAYING EGGS

IN SEPTEMBER 1986, IN GREENWICH, CONNECTICUT, A
FETID CARPET CONTAINING THE DECOMPOSING BODY OF
A YOUNG WOMAN IS DISCOVERED. THE VICTIM HAS BEEN
STABBED FIFTEEN TIMES. BLOWFLY LARVAE ARE SEEN
MOVING IN AND FEEDING ON THE CORPSE. THESE, ALONG
WITH BLOWFLY PUPARIA, ARE GATHERED FOR ANALYSIS IN
THE LABORATORY. A FORENSIC ENTOMOLOGIST IS ABLE
TO SPECIFY FROM THE INSECT EVIDENCE THAT BLOWFLIES
HAD LAID EGGS ON THE BODY SEVEN DAYS PREVIOUSLY.
A SUSPECT IS FOUND TO HAVE A MATCHING CARPET
PATTERN IN HIS HOME. THE CARPET AND INSECT
EVIDENCE ARE IMPORTANT CONTRIBUTING FACTORS
IN HIS SUBSEQUENT CONVICTION FOR MURDER.

OTHERS THAT SO FEAST
Beetles tend to appear when a body is in an extended
state of decomposition, and moth flies will often replace
them during the latter end of the process. Macrocheles
mites are often present during the very early stages of
decomposition. Tyroglyphidae and Oribatidae mites such
as Rostrozetes feast on the dry skin of a corpse in its
later stages of decomposition.

FOUR DAYS AGO

THE PARTIALLY CLAD BODY OF A YOUNG FEMALE IS FOUND ALONGSIDE A RURAL NORTHWESTERN U.S. HIGHWAY. AN AUTOPSY REVEALS THAT MULTIPLE HEAD AND NECK WOUNDS INFLICTED BY A HEAVY SHARP OBJECT CAUSED THE VICTIM'S DEATH.

POSTMORTEM INTERVAL ESTIMATES ARE OFFERED BY MEDICAL EXAMINERS AND INVESTIGATORS, BASED MAINLY ON THE PHYSICAL APPEARANCE OF THE CORPSE AND DECOMPOSITIONAL CHANGES IN VARIOUS ORGANS.

NUMEROUS FLY LARVAE (MAGGOTS), ADULT FLIES, AND OTHER INSECTS ARE OBSERVED AND COLLECTED IN AND AROUND THE VICTIM'S WOUNDS.

BASED ON THIS TOTAL ARRAY OF EVIDENCE, RANGING FROM CLIMATOLOGICAL DATA, MAXIMUM AND MINIMUM TEMPERATURES, AND WEATHER CONDITIONS, ENTOMOLOGISTS DETERMINE THAT THE FIRST INSECTS TO COLONIZE THE REMAINS ARRIVED FOUR DAYS EARLIER. AN ARMY SERGEANT LAST SEEN WITH THE GIRL IS CONVICTED AND SENTENCED TO LIFE WITHOUT PAROLE.

COCHLIOMYIA MACELLARIA

The body of a young white male is found in a sandy shrub habitat, in the southwestern United States. It is early spring. The victim has been shot with multiple small caliber bullet wounds to the chest and back. There is little external evidence of decomposition.

A tiny granular mass of blowfly eggs is retrieved from the surface of the victim's left eye. Several have already hatched. These maggots are Cochliomyia macellaria, the secondary screw worm. The developmental biology of this fly is known, and, taken in conjunction with climatic conditions, it is determined that the eggs were laid twenty-four to thirty-six hours prior to the discovery of the body. It is later discovered that the man's killer had murdered him approximately thirty-six hours prior to the finding of his corpse.

> ### DEAD FOR 18 DAYS
> It is late November and the partially clad corpse of a young black female is discovered by passing motorists in woodland in suburban Washington D.C. She has been stabbed multiple times in the neck and chest. Fully developed, postfeeding blowfly larvae are found on the body.
>
> Though there is much circumstantial evidence pointing to the suspect, accuracy as to time of death is essential. There are conflicting estimates of postmortem interval, varying from two to eight days, due to the extent of the autolytic changes occurring within various organs.

Climatological data is examined. Adult Calliphora vicina are found to have been present during the first few days following death.

Based on the entomological data it is determined that the victim had been dead eighteen days, and a suspect is arrested and later convicted.

OUT IN THE COLD

In the second week of December the remains of a white male are discovered under a bridge in southern Indiana. There is mild decomposition, with slight "skin slippage" on the arms and upper torso. Most of the victim's face is skeletonized. Several calliphorid larvae (Calliphora vomitoria) are found in the sinus and oral cavities of the face.

The Indiana temperatures were below average in October and above average in November and December. Blowfly larva development is analyzed and compared with pertinent climatological data. This suggests that it takes at least forty-eight days at the recorded daily maximum and minimum temperatures for the maggots to reach the size and stage found on the remains. Later in the investigation it is learned that the decedent had wandered away from a mental institution fifty-four days prior to the discovery of his corpse. He had succumbed to hypothermia and exposure during October.

28 DAYS EARLIER

South eastern U.S. police are called to investigate a foul-smelling odour emanating from a residence. Lying in a shallow grave in the dirt basement of the house, they discover the badly decomposed body of a young black woman.

The victim has been killed with a single bullet from a small caliber rifle wound to the head. Careful examination of the remains and a detailed excavation of the soil at the burial pit reveal the presence of numerous larvae of Calliphora vicina and larvae and pupae of Synthesiomyia nudesita—a relative of the housefly.

Specimens are examined at the laboratory. Supplemental information such as soil temperatures and climatic data are reviewed. Developmental biology of both species of fly colonization is twenty-eight days prior to the discovery of the remains.

Larvae of multiple fly species provide investigators with a scientifically reliable method of estimating the time of a person's death.

The murderer later confesses to murdering the woman twenty-eight days earlier.

THE BODY FARM

A very special outdoor laboratory, often referred to as the "Body Farm," is situated in the state of Tennessee. Sited on a two-acre plot of land densely populated by trees, the facility is surrounded by a tall and imposing fence. Inside the laboratory, lying in varying stages of decay, are more than forty human bodies. In order to assist the police, these bodies are studied closely over intervals of time by scientists, their aim being to view and record findings pertinent to what happens when bugs, animals and the weather take their toll on the corpse of a human being.

FORENSIC GEOLOGY

The chief recognized application of forensic geology is the use of samples such as trace evidence which can be vital in connecting a suspect to a crime scene. There are many ways in which the information collected can be applied including:

- The cause of death

(most useful in suffocation and drowning)

- How long a body has been present at the site
- Where an identified body came from
- The location of buried items (e.g., drugs, bodies)
- Was a person, a car, etc., at a specific location

(e.g., crime scene)?

THE IMPORTANCE OF DIRT
ACCORDING TO GROSS AND POPP

In 1893 Hans Gross, an Austrian professor of criminology, testifies to the importance of examining dirt on a suspect's shoes as an indication of where he has been. But the German chemist, Georg Popp, is widely recognized as being the first to conduct regulated "soil" comparison studies in the early nineteen hundreds.

At about the same time as Popp is conducting his research, Sir Arthur Conan Doyle also uses soil comparison in a case where, unlike his literary creation, Sherlock Holmes, he becomes a real-life detective. The work of Gross, Popp, and Conan Doyle make a great impression on Edmund Locard, who had been a student of forensic medicine and is now director of the Technical Police Laboratory in Lyons, France. He is responsible for the first extensive scientific policies for the analysis of dust traces.

STILL ALIVE

The burning body of a man who has been shot in the head is found on a farm track on the outskirts of Edinburgh, Scotland's capital city. Several particles of gravel have been gathered at postmortem from the bronchi and trachea of the victim. These are later traced to a river setting in an area near Glasgow. The deep penetration into the lungs and the comparatively large size of the particles indicate the gravel particles had been ingested while the victim was still alive. The suggestion is that he had been held face down under the water before being shot dead.

ONE WAY OF CONTESTING AN ALIBI

When soil is found on a suspect's shoe, a comparison can be made with samples taken from the scene of the crime, and if the individual suspected states that he was elsewhere (alibi) at the time the crime was being committed, then evidence from this location can be tested.

When properly utilized soil is solid associative evidence due to the multitudinous complex processes from which it is formed. As a result of this there is a huge variety in the composition of soil. The mineral content in conjunction with the biological content of soil can be analyzed and isolate a type of soil to a particular location.

THE SEAMSTRESS AND THE SOIL

An English seamstress called Eva Disch is found murdered in October 1904. At the scene of the homicide is found a filthy handkerchief that contains grains of a mineral called hornblend, along with bits of snuff and coal. Police suspect a man who works part-time at a quarry where the rock is rich in hornblend and also at a coal-burning gasworks. He has two layers of dirt in his trouser turnups. The bottom layer corresponds to the soil at the scene of the murder and the upper layer, notable for a distinct type of mica particle, corresponds to the soil found on the path leading to the victim's home. When presented with this evidence the suspect quickly confesses.

*GREEN GOOSE DROPPINGS AND A CASE OF
EXAMINING SHOES*

*In 1908 in Bavaria, investigators are examining
geological aspects in the murder of Margarethe Filbert.
The man accused of her killing farms in nearby fields
that have pieces of mica, milky quartz and porphyry
contained within the soil. The land surrounding the
suspect's home is littered with green goose droppings,
and the soil at the murder scene contains red clay and
red quartz. When the homicide suspect's shoes are
examined they are found to be covered with particles
of red quartz and clay and a layer of green goose
droppings. Unfortunately for the accused, who claims
to have been working in the fields at the time of the
murder, they bear no traces of mica, milky quartz
or porphyry!*

FORENSIC BOTANY

Forensic botany is the application of plant science in
order to determine the answers to legal questions;
this discipline is comparatively recent. Forensic
botany comprises various subdivisions of plant
science: dendrochronology (study of tree rings),
palynology (study of pollen), systematics (expertise in
the identification of drugs, importantly marijuana), ecology
(expertise here is helpful in specifying whether fragments
from plants retrieved from a victim or object came
from where it was discovered or somewhere else), and
limnology (study of freshwater ecology, including diatoms).

WHERE DID HE COME FROM?

An unidentified illegal immigrant to the U.K. is found in the wheel well of a Boeing 747 airplane which lands at Heathrow Airport. Unfortunately, since the wheel well had last been properly examined, the plane had made several flights to different countries. This is narrowed down to three places where it would have been possible to stow away. Red soil from the immigrant's boots is examined using a combination of techniques which suggest it originates from a wet tropical country. Prior to arriving at Heathrow the plane had departed from Ghana, and samples are taken from a location there. It is deduced that an extremely high degree of similarity between all comparison criteria is present.

THE PALOVERDE TREES

In Maricopa County, Arizona, in May 1992, a woman's body is found in an abandoned factory. A man is arrested but vehemently denies having been at the scene. However, from the back of his truck, police collect seed pods from a paloverde tree for analysis. A geneticist finds that the paloverde trees produce great genetic variability and as such are easily distinguished from each other. Using several trees chosen at random, the seed pods are matched to the tree at the crime scene. This proves the suspect's truck had been there and the evidence is incisive enough to be admissible in court.

SUBTERRANEAN SECRETS

When attempting to find a hidden grave a forensic scientist, with his superior knowledge of plant succession, can be of great assistance to the investigator. A burial disturbs the soil and lays it bare—but not for long. Trailblazing species quickly appropriate the site, followed by later-succession species. If a particular site shows a different successional stage to its neighboring area, there is a good chance it is a possible burial site. This irregularity in vegetation can still be detected two decades later.

THE LAST SUPPER?

Intrinsic cell types from food plants can determine what a victim's last meal comprised. This information can help to reveal the victim's actions or whereabouts prior to death.

A young woman has been stabbed to death and witnesses testify that she had eaten her last meal at a particular restaurant. At autopsy, however, no match can be found between the restaurant's menu and the contents of the dead woman's stomach; evidently she had eaten some time after she had been observed at the restaurant. The subsequent investigation leads to the arrest of a man known to the victim. It is with this man she had shared her actual last meal.

ARTISTIC LICENSE

OLD MASTERS OFTEN PAINTED DIRECTLY ONTO WOOD RATHER THAN CANVAS. TREE RING ANALYSIS IS A COMMON METHOD FOR DATING THESE PAINTINGS AND, PROVIDED THAT SAMPLES ARE IN A REASONABLE CONDITION, ANALYSTS ARE ABLE TO SPECIFY THE EXACT YEAR WHEN THE TREE, USED FOR THE WOOD FOR THE PAINTING, WAS FELLED. SO DEFINITIVE IS THIS TECHNIQUE THAT A PAINTED WALL PANEL IN A HOUSE IN SWITZERLAND IN THE 1970S WAS DEEMED TO HAVE BEEN PAINTED ON SPRUCE CUT DOWN IN 1497. OBVIOUSLY WHEN IT COMES TO THE QUESTION OF ART FRAUD, TREE RING ANALYSIS IS A CRUCIAL TOOL.

FORENSIC PALYNOLOGY

This is the branch of science concerned with the study of pollen, spores, and similar palynomorphs, living and fossil. Etymonl: Greek "to strew or sprinkle," is suggestive of "fine meal," cognate with Latin *pollen*, "fine flour, dust."

THE O.J. SIMPSON CASE: COULD A POLLEN "FINGERPRINT" HAVE HELPED CATCH A KILLER?

The murder trial of former U.S. football star and movie actor O.J. Simpson concludes in October 1995. The jury finds him innocent.

Simpson has been accused of killing his wife, Nicole, and her friend Ronald Goldman in a manic frenzy, allegedly driven by jealousy and rage. During the court proceedings, many important items entered into evidence are forensic samples of hair, fibers, and DNA from bloodstained clothing and blood discovered at the crime scene, in the defendant's car, and at his residence.

It is suggested at the trial that the person or persons responsible for the killings may have hidden in bushes before striking. But the prosecution and defense miss the forensic pollen evidence associated with this. If the clothing supposedly worn by Simpson on the night of the murders had been examined it might have contained certain types of pollen from flowers on the bushes.

FORENSIC RADIOLOGY

Radiology is a potent tool for the forensic investigator because it creates images of what is hidden inside the body. Using, among other technologies, magnetic resonance imaging (MRI), computed tomography (CT), and X-rays, scientists can trace projectile paths inside the body. They can make three-dimensional images of the human form, helping identify victims whose remains are badly damaged. "Forensic radiology comprises the performance, interpretation, and reporting of those radiologic examinations and procedures that concern the courts and/or the law."

(B.G. Brogden, M.D., American Professor of Radiology, 1998)

Most people were unaware that radiology as a forensic science existed. But after such disasters as the tsunami in Thailand, the Oklahoma City Bombings, Hurricane Katrina, and the World Trade Center disaster and the subsequent identification efforts, radiology is now making a name for itself.

MCVEIGH X-RAY

Timothy McVeigh, who receives the death penalty for his role in the murder of one hundred and sixty-eight people in the Oklahoma City Bombings, refuses, before his execution by lethal injection in 2001, to allow an autopsy to be performed. Interestingly, he does agree to a non-invasive X-ray autopsy.

FINDING ITS PLACE

Some uses of forensic radiology include:

- Body identification

  In conjunction with DNA and dental analysis, radiographic images can be utilized. This involves obtaining, if possible, any investigations carried out before death such as CT scans or X-rays from a suspect and comparing distinguishing anatomical details with similar postmortem examinations.

- Suspicious death/murder

  Radiographic technology can assist the pathologist in specifying the cause of death, possibly making them aware of an unanticipated suspicious death, in which case the autopsy technique may differ.

- Drug trafficking

  It is not unusual for drug traffickers to swallow or cavity-insert drugs in protective wrappers (body packing) to avoid detection. CT scans can identify these packages, thereby assisting law enforcement agencies in screening suspects.

THE DRUG OF CHOICE

The use/abuse of cocaine continues to increase but considering the basic pharmacology of cocaine and its metabolites (including cocaethylene), it's strange that it is often referred to as a "safe drug." It is the opinion of forensic experts that this is far from true: the forensic psychiatrist, who sees chronic abuse and the psychiatric effects of cocaine intoxication; the forensic pathologist, who investigates the death of a drug abuser both at autopsy and the scene of death; both refute the "safeness" of cocaine.

A SHOCK DEATH

In 1901 President William McKinley is shot twice, at close range, with a .32 caliber revolver. One bullet hits him in the stomach and the other grazes his sternum. A hastily conducted operation takes place at the small local hospital. The surgeon retrieves the bullet lodged in his stomach and closes the incision with a needle and thread. They are unable to locate the second bullet.

A concerned McKinley aide contacts Thomas Edison and tells him to bring his X-ray machine to the hospital as a matter of urgency. He does, but doctors think it unnecessary. They are convinced the president is improving and predict a full recovery—but he dies.

The lost bullet is recovered during the autopsy but it is only indirectly responsible for McKinley's death—gangrene has developed along the route of the bullet. The president had died of septic shock due to bacterial infection.

2006 and a World-First Forensic Technique

It is believed that a team led by a forensic pathologist at the University of Leicester, England, is the first to utilize a new radiological system for the investigation of mass fatality. Up until now there have been two types of radiology used—plain x-ray and fluoroscopy. But the professor and his team have employed a mobile MSCT scanner in the mortuary for the investigation into victims of a road accident resulting in mass fatalities. In comparison with the more traditional systems, this approach proved to be faster and provided superior information on identification, cause of death, autopsy planning, and health and safety.

THE DOVER TEAM

IT IS SEPTEMBER 11, 2001 AND AFTER THE TERRORIST ATTACKS IN THE UNITED STATES A FORENSIC TEAM AT THE DOVER, DEL., MORTUARY ARE GIVEN THE SAD TASK OF IDENTIFYING THE 189 VICTIMS OF THE PENTAGON ATTACK. THEY WORK TWELVE HOURS A DAY, SEVEN DAYS A WEEK, AND THE DOVER RADIOLOGY MILITARY TEAM ARE OUTSTANDING. THEY GO ABOUT THEIR UNENVIABLE DUTIES QUIETLY AND PROFESSIONALLY. "THE RADIOGRAPHIC ANALYSIS OF THE REMAINS WAS A CRUCIAL STEP IN THE IDENTIFICATION OF THE VICTIMS, AND WAS ALSO AN AID TO THE FBI INVESTIGATION OF THE CRIME SCENE." (THOMAS E. HASTINGS)

Setting the Scene

"Forensic analysis of evidence found at the crime scene is crucial to determinations of guilt or innocence."
The FBI's *Handbook of Forensic Services*

THE CRIME SCENE

Crime scene experts focus their efforts on support for law enforcement agencies in the investigation of serious crimes. The reconstruction of a crime scene and/or bloodstain pattern investigation can also be used to go beyond the usual question of "Who did it?" to questions like "Could it have been suicide?" or "Was it self-defense?"

Initially, before anything else is attempted, the physical evidence must be collected in a proper manner. In order for this to happen, the crime scene containing the physical evidence must be protected and secured. These safeguards are the responsibility of all law enforcement workers who come into contact with the victim, suspect, or indeed the scene.

CRIMINALISTICS

The job of the criminalist, usually a laboratory scientist, is to analyze trace evidence associated with a crime. The results are used as evidence in a court of law. Trace evidence includes paint, explosives, vegetation, fire debris, fibers, gunshot residues, hair, bodily fluids, glass, and metal. Criminalists are also concerned with voice patterns, firearms and ballistics, computer files, imprints, and documents.

SKETCH OF DEATH

Often, once a scene has been photographed, the investigator will sketch the crime scene. This will comprise measurements of the body and the scene containing it. Beginning as a rough sketch it will be fleshed out to create a scene sketch, to scale, and may be used as a mock-up in court. There are four sorts of sketches: a) elevation sketch: viewing the scene from the side; b) overhead sketch: a type of aerial photo sometimes referred to as a "bird's-eye view;" c) exploded view sketch: named for the way it depicts what would happen if the inside of the room exploded and the walls collapsed outwards; d) perspective sketch: involving some artistic skills, this adds a third dimension to the scene.

TAGGED AS CRITICAL

Once photographs and sketches have been completed at the crime scene, delicate items of evidence are collected. Weston and Lushbaugh (2003) place evidence found at the scene in seven categories: a) dust and dirt traces; b) blood; c) impressions or imprints; d) weapons; e) questioned documents; f) tool marks; g) varieties of transfer or trace evidence.

All items are tagged but particular care is taken over critical evidence, like a weapon, which should be tagged with the detective's mark, as it may well form the basis of his future testimony in court.

FURTHER SKETCHED

When it comes to the body, detectives at the scene are permitted only to make sketches or conduct non-intrusive investigations such as, e.g., perfunctory examination of injuries, smelling for odors, studying the eyes.

Death scene investigators have the sole right to closely examine injuries. In order to preserve evidence the body is usually wrapped in a sheet, placed in a body bag, and transported to the morgue. If the victim is not identified his fingerprints are taken, a DNA profile is sought and dental records from local surgeries are checked. Sometimes local restaurants are contacted to ascertain the last meal eaten (this will be included in the autopsy report). If all this fails a physical description is run past a Missing Persons database along with an appeal for help on the part of the media.

STAGING

In an attempt to stage a crime scene the offender commonly makes errors in striving to arrange the scene to simulate what they think it should look like. He is tense and anxious, not always able to fit all the pieces together in a logical manner. Because of this, irregularities in forensic discoveries and the overall scene will occur. These irregularities will be viewed as danger signals and reflect that staging may have taken place, guarding the detective against misjudgments.

BETRAYED EVEN UNTO DEATH
A man returning home unexpectedly surprises burglars. As they make their escape the man is killed. Investigators determine that nothing is stolen. The intruders had, however, begun the task of dismantling a large TV and video unit in the man's home. More careful examination indicates that less cumbersome and more valuable objects such as jewelry and a coin collection are left. The conclusion is that the victim's wife is having an affair with one of the burglars and she has paid them to stage the crime and murder her husband.

THE SEARCH FOR A BODY

When the search for a missing person becomes a search for a body, the investigator must be prepared for the following if the body is lying somewhere unburied:

• The ground could be covered with leaves at seasonal times and this will increase the time it takes to make the discovery.

• Animal and insect activity and the climate could result in extreme decomposition.

• Partial or entire self-burial: loosened teeth and small bones can sink below the surface as rain, wind, and insects do their work, causing agitation of the soil, and fallen leaves cover the body.

• The dispersal of bones by birds or wild animals—even gravity plays a part if the remains are on a slope.

DECOMPOSITION

Decomposition begins at the time of death and is influenced by the clothing worn by the deceased at the time. Dressed in light clothes it will take several months for disarticulation to occur. Heavier clothing will prolong the time. The process of decomposition is complete when only hard tissues like bone and teeth remain. After a year, the chances of recovery are small because most bones will have been scattered. The location and variables such as weather, natural land movement or animal predation will also affect decomposition.

DISMEMBERMENT

Unless a particular murderer derives some form of pleasure from the act of cutting to pieces a human being, the purpose behind dismemberment will most probably be a means of practicality in terms of rendering a larger, heavier body into smaller manageable pieces in preparation for disposal. A victim's head will often be severed and disposed of separately as a means to confound later potential discovery of a victim's remains.

THE TRUTH ABOUT LIME

Alfred Lucas experiments with lime on dead flesh. He is the first forensic scientist to do so and his systematic evaluation of the effects of different forms of lime determines that lime is a preservative first and foremost. He also takes into account "slaking"—absorption of the body's own waters from its burial soil, resulting in partial desiccation of soft tissues. Lucas concludes that quicklime does not destroy a body but rather retards putrefaction. So lime in fact has quite the opposite effect to that which one sees in the movies!

A FATEFUL MISCALCULATION

Fourteen years before Jack the Ripper makes his bloody and indelible mark on the Whitechapel area of East London, Henry Wainwright decides that enough is enough—in the most final of ways—and shoots dead his increasingly bothersome mistress, Harriet Lane.

Dragging her corpse into his workshop he inters the body after packing it in a half hundredweight of chlorinated lime. The lime preserves Miss Lane's body remarkably well making the physician's job exceptionally easy when tasked with identifying the remains after their discovery the following year.

Despite decomposition hastening slaking of the flesh, twelve points of identification are successfully matched and it is off to the gallows with Mr. Wainwright.

QUICKLIME

Swiss-born Maria de Roux is traveling from England to meet her friend on the Continent. Her journey brings her face to face with a forty-nine-year-old Irishman and Customs Officer named Patrick O'Connor. Maria later marries a career criminal masquerading as a railroad guard for the Great Western Railway named Frederick George Manning. Manning and de Roux soon conspire to murder O'Connor—financial motives such as greed being paramount in their diabolical design—with whom de Roux has been having an affair.

Shot and battered to death with a ripping chisel, O'Connor's body is doused with quicklime and buried underneath the kitchen flagstones. The corpse is easily identifiable despite the couple's erroneous belief that the quicklime will hasten decomposition. They are both hanged in November 1849 at Horsemonger Lane Gaol.

LIGHT AND SILVER SALTS

In 1724, in Germany, Johann Heinrich Schultze notes that silver salts darken when light is shone upon them. He has just discovered the principle behind photographic film. This will of course be refined over the coming decades, but Schultze's intriguing finding sets the precedent.

JOHN GEORGE HAIGH AND THE ACID THAT DISSOLVED HIS CONFIDENCE

Notorious British archfiend John George Haigh's career is charming rich women out of their fortunes before murdering them and dissolving their bodies in acid. As no bodies remain, Haigh believes he cannot be tried for murder. He even brags to friends about his crimes telling them that all that's left of Mrs. Olivia Durand-Deacon is a layer of "sludge."

Dr. Keith Simpson believes that he can get results from the "sludge" and analyzes it. Simpson finds, among traces of human fat, evidence of dentures and a gallstone that can be identified as belonging to Mrs. Durand-Deacon. The arrogant Haigh, dubbed by the Press "the Acid Bath Murderer" is of course hanged for his atrocities. Alfred Pierrepoint does the honors.

THE FIRST DAGUERREOTYPE

France, 1826, and retired army officer Joseph Nicephore Niepce experiments with a beam of light focused on a light-sensitive bitumen solution. It takes eight years to complete the exposure. Later partnering with Louis Daguerre, he uses a copperplate coated with silver iodide along with a mercury vapor-developed image on an exposed plate, and the first "daguerreotype" or photograph is produced.

MALCOLM ANDERS IS A FRAUD—FOR MORE THAN A DECADE HE HAS PRETENDED TO BE DISABLED AFTER AN ACCIDENT AT WORK. IT IS JUST BEFORE CHRISTMAS 2000 AND MRS. ANDERS IS FOUND LYING DEAD ON THE KITCHEN FLOOR. HER HUSBAND TELLS THE POLICE ABOUT AN INTRUDER WHO HAS PUSHED HIM OVER AFTER STABBING HIS WIFE.

MERSEYSIDE DETECTIVES CAN FIND NO SIGN OF A FORCED ENTRY AND, QUITE UNUSUALLY FOR A BURGLARY, NOTHING IS MISSING. FORENSIC SCIENTISTS FROM TWO LABORATORIES ARE INVOLVED, ONE OF WHOM HAS COME TO THE CRIME SCENE TWICE TO INVESTIGATE BECAUSE HE FEELS SOMETHING "IS NOT QUITE RIGHT."

DESPITE THE FACT THAT ANDERS INSISTS THE HOUSE HAS BEEN BURGLED EVERYTHING SEEMS SO NEAT AND TIDY, AND IT IS OBVIOUS ATTEMPTS HAVE BEEN MADE TO MOVE THE BODY AND CLEAN UP. THREE FSS SCIENTISTS GIVE EVIDENCE AT LIVERPOOL CROWN COURT AND THE JURY FIND ANDERS GUILTY OF HIS WIFE'S MURDER. ALTHOUGH ANDERS OCCUPIES A WHEELCHAIR THROUGHOUT THE PROCEEDINGS, HIS DOCTOR SAYS THERE IS NO EVIDENCE OF MUSCLE WASTAGE IN HIS LEGS AND THE JUDGE TELLS HIM HE IS "A CLEVER, MANIPULATIVE MAN." HE RECEIVES A LIFE SENTENCE.

A PICTURE IS WORTH A THOUSAND WORDS

Although the principle of photography has been around since the eighteenth century, it is not until the 1850s, when the wet and dry plates are invented, that photography is made easier and reproduction from a negative film is possible. Quickly realizing the impact this will have on criminal cases, the authorities almost immediately begin to use the camera to capture images of crime scenes, injuries, or fatalities caused to victims, and in some cases the faces of suspects.

THE ROGUES' GALLERIES

In 1886, New York police detective, Thomas Byrnes, publishes what is believed to be the first "rogues' gallery," a collection of many full-face photographs of known criminals. These prototypes of what will become familiarly known as "mug shots" are essential to future criminal investigations—by publishing these collections victims of crime may be able to identify the perpetrator by recognizing his or her face in the gallery.

MISSED BY THE NAKED EYE

Forensic photography assists the forensic scientist, toxicologist and medical examiner by recording crime scenes, evidence, and autopsies. The forensic photography department also bears responsibility for the creation of graphics for the court, exhibitions, training, and the Internet.

Several methods are employed in supporting the search for evidence because not everything can be seen by the naked eye. For example, infrared film is used to document gunshot residue on clothing; different wavelengths of light can cause some fibers to become fluorescent, and ultraviolet light records the presence of semen.

MEASUREMENTS

Many aspects of forensic photography have been enhanced by new digital imaging techniques. The methods that were once experimentally applied in the darkroom can now be applied on a computer and therefore results are seen immediately on the screen. One new technique now available, used by the forensic photography department, is the capability of correcting the perspective of an image. This is critical when a case demands measurements are taken of the evidence in an image.

- The appearance of evidence seen in the photograph not discovered previously.
- Poorly perceived bruises and wounds can be improved so a forensic pathologist can investigate more thoroughly.
- Imperfect photographs can be improved to make the image more visible.
- Physical evidence can be matched against existing photographs.
- In complicated crime scenes demonstrations to the jury clarify information.

AT THE SCENE OF THE CRIME

Upon arrival at the crime scene, photographs should be taken as soon as all evidence is tagged for that purpose. Crime scene photographs are in both black-and-white and color, also in both analog and digital. Standard cameras are usually single lens reflex or auto-focusing and exposure SLR. Photographers will use a variety of measuring implements to put in the photographs and extra lighting or extension flashes to bathe the scene in light.

STEADYING THE SHOT

Tripods are used to keep the shots steady. At a crime scene the digital camera must have close-up capabilities, a flash attachment, and a minimum of four megapixels. When photographing very small pieces of evidence, obviously finer detail is achieved by using more pixels.

PHOTOGRAPHIC OVERVIEW

At the scene two photographs of each shot should be captured in the event one is blurred. The type of photographs taken should be:

Overview: i.e., location and approach.

Midrange (ten to twelve feet): to build up a picture for the investigator, assisting in the establishment of the offender's modus operandi.

Close-up: vital in establishing the corpus delicti—the tangible evidence of the crime, e.g., the corpse.

Generally there are two systems of photography:
a) Progressive: starting with a fixed point and photographing items of evidence while progressively moving toward it.
b) Overlapping: a number of shots taken in a circular direction, overlapping slightly to capture the overall scene.

MURDER WEAPONS

THE IMPLEMENT USED AS THE MURDER WEAPON CAN YIELD CRUCIAL EVIDENCE SUCH AS FINGERPRINTS, THE ORIGIN OF THE MURDERER AND POSSIBLY THE MOTIVE. GUNS AND NOW EXPLOSIVES HAVE BECOME A HUGE DANGER AND ARE INCREASINGLY USED BECAUSE OF THEIR ABILITY TO CREATE MASS DESTRUCTION. POISON, THE SILENT KILLER, FITS INTO THIS CATEGORY AS DO, SURPRISINGLY, MOTOR VEHICLES.

HOW DID THE FIRE START?

When investigating how a fire started the signs to look for include the depth of burning, flaking of materials such as plaster or cement, lingering heat, distorted glass, metal, and plastic caused by sustained burning and any structural damage. Only once the location where a fire started is discovered can investigators begin their search for what caused it.

THE IGNITION FACTOR

Arsonists usually use something to accelerate the burning process, petrol, for example, and a fire-starting implement to ignite the fire. This device can be anything from a match to an intricate electric timer. Fortunately, whatever the device or accelerant, it often survives the fire. If investigators fail to see or smell it, they use "hydrocarbon" detectors. Anything doubtful is sent to the laboratory for analysis.

EXPLOSION

AT THE SCENE OF AN EXPLOSION, SPECIALLY TRAINED OFFICERS MUST IDENTIFY AND COLLECT EVIDENCE. IT IS OF COURSE VITAL THAT MATERIAL SO RECOVERED REMAINS UNCONTAMINATED AND PROPERLY LABELED FOR LABORATORY EXAMINATION.

VARIOUS SUBSTANCES OR RELEVANT ITEMS MUST BE COLLECTED AND TAKEN FOR CHEMISTRY LABORATORY ANALYSIS. OF MAJOR IMPORTANCE IS THE RECOVERY OF ANY EXPLOSIVES OR MATERIALS LEFT UNDETONATED IN THE EXPLOSION. SOFT AND POROUS MATERIALS SUCH AS FURNISHINGS, WOOD, AND SOIL ARE CLOSELY INSPECTED AS EVIDENCE WILL OF COURSE HAVE BEEN SCATTERED ACROSS A WIDE RADIUS FOLLOWING AN EXPLOSION AND IT IS NECESSARY TO RECOVER EVERY LAST SHRED OF BOMB DEBRIS, WHICH MUST THEN BE SIFTED, MOST COMMONLY USING A FINE WIRE MESH.

CARS AS WEAPONS

Yes, even automobiles are sometimes used as weapons. Investigators need to know in what direction a vehicle was moving, how fast it was traveling and whether the driver had attempted to brake. This is where the forensic scientist plays a vital role by gathering and analyzing evidence in an effort to reconstruct exactly what happened.

The locations of any skid marks, recording of measurements and drawings of the road must all be collated. Along with the type of car and any photographs taken from an angle where a computer can reveal the distance of the road marks, all this is prepared for computer reconstruction. Once complete the reconstructed animation is admissible in court.

BOMBS

When a bomb explodes fragments are often scattered far away from the scene. But even though these fragments can be minute, they can still direct investigators to the bomb's manufacturer. All over the world explosive units keep a huge supply of frequently used bomb parts such as remote control devices, batteries, timers, and fuel components, enabling experts to find similarities between specific blasts.

THE MAGUIRES

THE MAGUIRE FAMILY, CONSISTING OF SIX MEMBERS, ARE CONVICTED OF RUNNING AN IRA BOMB FACTORY. THEY ARE ALSO FOUND GUILTY OF POSSESSING FIREARMS AND ARE EACH GIVEN PRISON TERMS RANGING FROM FOUR TO FOURTEEN YEARS. THEY ARE CONVICTED ON JUST ONE PIECE OF EVIDENCE: A TEST USING SWABS FROM RUBBER GLOVES TAKEN FROM THE MAGUIRES IS CARRIED OUT AT THE ROYAL ARMAMENT RESEARCH AND DEVELOPMENT ESTABLISHMENT WHICH SCIENTIFICALLY (THROUGH THE USE OF THIN-LAYER CHROMATOGRAPHY) DEMONSTRATES THAT TRACES OF NITROGLYCERINE ARE PRESENT ON THE ALLEGED BOMB-MAKERS' HANDS.

ALTHOUGH THIS APPEARS TO DAMN THEM, IT IS ALSO A FACT THAT HAD THE FAMILY BEEN HANDLING ANGINA TABLETS, WHICH CONTAIN ANOTHER EXPLOSIVE, PETN, THE TEST WOULD HAVE ALSO PROVED CONCLUSIVE. THIS BEING THE ONLY DIRECT EVIDENCE AGAINST THE MAGUIRES, IN 1990 THE COURT OF APPEAL OVERTURNS THEIR CONVICTIONS.

These are injuries resulting from sharp instruments like knives, daggers, and nails. The type of knife used is often determined by the sort of wound it inflicts on the body, i.e., serrated-edged, single-edged, or double-edged knives. Serrated knives leave a rough edge around the wound; single-edged knives have one sharp edge and leave wounds with a boat-like shape; double-edged knives leave markings of two sharp edges.

BLUNT TRAUMA

Common in varying types of violent assault, these are injuries resulting from blunt instruments like rocks, ornaments, and baseball bats. Evidence of blunt trauma is seen in injuries such as bruising and broken bones. Fractures and fatalities often lie just around the corner with these kinds of attacks.

SCENT DOWN

Without warning a fifteen-year-old girl is approached by a man who drags her into nearby woods and rapes her. The girl can't remember the exact location and the Canine Unit are called in. Both victim and attacker would have produced adrenal-related secretions, and the ground where the victim is dragged will undoubtedly bear the most disruption and chemical breakdowns that create scent patterns. Handler and dog go quickly to work and in a clearing find the girl's underclothes. The forensic services unit is able to obtain traces of semen at the scene for DNA matching which leads to the apprehension of the perpetrator. The dog has done its job well.

EAGLE

A Doberman–shorthaired-pointer mix called Eagle and his handler, Sandra Anderson, are trailblazers in the field of using dogs to find human remains. They have many successes over the years in finding evidence in murders and even locating old Native American burial grounds. But as Eagle gets older his senses fail, and in order to maintain her celebrity status it is alleged Anderson planted evidence, including smearing a hacksaw with her own blood and hiding bones from a dissected foot belonging to a friend of hers, at a number of purported crime scenes. In 2004 she pleads guilty to five counts of falsifying evidence.

DOG DNA

NOT UNCOMMONLY, ANIMAL HAIRS ARE FOUND AT CRIME SCENES AND ON A VICTIM'S BODY OR CLOTHING. DNA PROFILING REVEALS THE UNIQUE IDENTITY OF AN INDIVIDUAL DOG. THE PROFILE IS OBTAINED FROM HALF MATERNAL AND HALF PATERNAL SOURCES, PROVIDING PARENTAGE AND INDIVIDUAL IDENTIFICATION. CURRENTLY MOST CRIME LABS DO NOT POSSESS THE TECHNOLOGY TO ANALYZE HAIR SAMPLES AND MTDNA AND SAMPLES ARE SENT ELSEWHERE—TO THE FBI, FOR EXAMPLE. BUT AS THIS TECHNOLOGY BECOMES CHEAPER, EXTRACTING DNA FROM HAIR AND OBTAINING A PROFILE WILL BECOME MORE COMMON. "THE HAIRS OF DOMESTIC CATS AND DOGS APPEAR FREQUENTLY AS TRANSFER EVIDENCE. WITH AN MTDNA DATABASE IT BECOMES POSSIBLE TO ASSESS THE EVIDENTIARY VALUE OF MTDNA COMPARISONS OF KNOWN AND QUESTIONED DOG HAIRS," SAYS WALTER ROWE, PROFESSOR OF FORENSIC SCIENCE.

Toxic Substances and Death Signs

"All substances are poisons; there is none which is not a poison. The right dose differentiates a poison and a remedy."
Paracelsus (1493-1541)

TYPES OF POISON:

ATROPINE

Atropine is extracted from deadly nightshade and other fungi and causes headaches, dizziness, hallucinations, and in heavy cases will induce a comatose state. It will be noted that the victim will die from heart or respiratory failure. The telltale sign of atropine poisoning is that the pupils dilate to such an extent that the whole eye can appear to be black.

POISON HEMLOCK

Poison hemlock can prove very difficult to discover when used in the commission of a murder. It causes numbness, which steadily increases until the heart fails or breathing stops. Poison hemlock produces almost exactly the same symptoms as one would find in an instance of suffocation.

ACONITINE

Aconitine was originally used to relieve the pain of rheumatism. When worn as a poultice against the skin it produces a warming anaesthetic. It is, also however, one of the most deadly poisons known to man. Even the smallest of amounts absorbed into the skin or swallowed can paralyze all the body's internal organs in rapid succession until death occurs by suffocation or heart failure.

THALLIUM

Thallium is a very useful poison for would-be murderers. Thallium dissolves invisibly and tastelessly in water and also causes symptoms that could easily be confused with influenza. The poison substitutes itself for potassium in the body and feeds nerve fibers and cells, causing the victim to become weaker and eventually die of cumulative internal organ failure. The one drawback for a potential murderer utilizing thallium as his means of dispatch is that it is a poison that in many cases will cause the victim's hair to fall out, and this is a fairly identifiable indicator of what has been used.

ANTIMONY

When antimony is administered in repeated doses, it can cause symptoms common to many stomach diseases, and as a result it is often missed by medical examiners and not attributed to poisoning. In the case of antimony being present within the body of a victim he will experience loss of appetite, sickness, stomach cramps, and diarrhoea, which can also lead to convulsions, depression, and ultimately heart failure and death.

ARSENIC

Arsenic is one of the more famous types of poison and is the subject of many an Agatha Christie literary or celluloid plot-line. In small doses, its symptoms can be mistaken for extreme food poisoning, cholera, and dysentery. As arsenic is an irritant, victims suffer from a burning sensation occurring within the throat, and also from stomach cramps and pains, nausea and sickness. However, arsenic can easily be detected in autopsies, as after a relatively short period of time traces of the poison can be discovered in all body tissues.

CYANIDE

Made famous—or infamous—by suicidal members of the Nazi Party hierarchy seeking to escape justice or retribution at the end of WWII, and also used by the California serial killer, Leonard Lake, to duck out of this world, thus avoiding punishment for his atrocities, cyanide is an exceptionally fast-working poison that kills its victim by rapidly depriving the blood of oxygen. Cyanide can be detected in the stomach's contents and is also distinctive in that it leaves a bitter smell of almonds in the mouths of victims, present for some time after death.

STRYCHNINE

Strychnine is a very potent poison, proving fatal at doses of just under one thousandth of an ounce. A most horrible death to witness, let alone endure, strychnine will cause violent muscle contractions and spasms, the victim's jaw muscles becoming paralyzed and thus rendering calls for help impossible. Within minutes the respiratory system is completely paralyzed, causing immediate death. Before reliable tests for poison were developed, many murders by such foul means were often mistaken for extreme epileptic fits.

THE UMBRELLA MURDER

On September 7, 1978, Bulgarian writer Georgi Markov, returning from work with the BBC World Service, feels a jab in his thigh. Turning, he sees a man stooping to pick up an umbrella. He tragically dies four days later in hospital.

He has an astonishing white blood cell count in excess of 500 million per cubic inch, over three times the normal level. A pellet less than one tenth of an inch is extracted from his thigh. It is found to contain a toxin—0.00001 of an ounce of ricin. The man suspected of masterminding the murder, Vasil Kotsev, later dies in an unexplained car accident before he can be brought to trial. The case remains unsolved.

It is impossible for the forensic toxicologist to classify all chemicals as either safe or poisonous. A crucial principle in toxicology is the "dose-response relationship." There are levels of dose-response relationship in the individual, and "quantal dose-response relationship" in the population as a whole. The latter is the most important because it is employed to find out the "median lethal dose" (MLD) and estimate what percentage of the population is affected by an increase in dose. "Quantal" means "all or none" and hence is the nearest thing to determining whether a substance is safe or poisonous.

FORENSIC TOXICOLOGY AND THE MURDER/SUICIDE METHOD OF CHOICE

Because many poisons imitate medical diseases, this has always proved a popular means of murder. Some natural substances only become poisonous when used in large quantities, and as a result of this it is sometimes difficult to distinguish between accidental death and murder in the case of an overdose. Toxicological screening is performed in 1962 when Marilyn Monroe is found dead. She did use drugs to combat depression and despite several conspiracy theories, the autopsy results determine accidental death. Though the mystery will doubtless endure, scientifically this high-profile case has long been answered.

TOXICOLOGY AND HAIR

The use of hair in toxicology studies is important, as hair remains when flesh has long disintegrated. Unless hair is eroded with acid or alkali, or burned, it will remain as evidence long after everything else organic has perished. It is often due to the endurance of a clump or even a single strand of hair and its analytical accuracy value upon retrieval that this type of evidence is presented during the legal proceedings of a particular case.

AIR EMBOLISM

The enduring myth that a bubble of air entering the bloodstream during an injection from a syringe can cause death can also be quickly dispelled. A 10cc syringe will not have such a lethal effect on a healthy and able-bodied person. The size of a fatal injection varies between 50cc and 300cc. At a life-threatening volume the injected air will form bubbles creating froth within the heart, resulting in an air-lock. It can also result in further bubbles reaching other vital organs such as the lungs and the brain. Regardless, death will come quickly for a victim.

NAPOLEON WAS POISONED

Technology and hair may have solved one of the most famous cases of poisoning. Napoleon Bonaparte, emperor of France, is well known for a painting done of him which features his hand inside his shirt covering his stomach. Napoleon had a habit of placing his hand over his stomach, leading others to deduce that he may have suffered from stomach cancer. His father had earlier died of this very illness.

Napoleon had written that he was being poisoned by his British captors. After he had died his valet retained a lock of his hair. With the advent of new technology the lock of hair which had survived was tested using neutron activation analysis. He was found to have been poisoned with a large quantity of arsenic, administered over a four-month period.

THE BORGIAS

The Borgias are one of the most notorious families of fifteenth- and sixteenth-century Italy. The infamous poisoners are Cesare Borgia and Lucrezia Borgia. These two are the illegitimate son and daughter of Rodrigo Borgia who went on to become Pope Alexander VI in 1492.

The pair dispatch several of their victims with a secret poison called "la cantarella." Nobody is really sure of its composition but it is probably a mixture of subacetate of copper, arsenic, and crude phosphorus. An Italian anecdote of the time comments that a person might say, "I am dining with the Borgias tonight," but nobody is able to say, "I dined last night with the Borgias!"

A MURDEROUS DUO

MOST POISONERS DERIVE A PERVERSE PLEASURE FROM THEIR LETHAL EXPLOITS AND LIKE TO WORK ALONE. THE MARQUISE DE BRINVILLIERS AND HER MALE LOVER SAINTE-CROIX WORKED TOGETHER.

DISCOVERING A COMMON PASSION FOR THE USE OF DEADLY POISONS, THEY SOON BEGIN EXPERIMENTING WITH CONCOCTIONS PILFERED FROM A SWISS APOTHECARY. A NUMBER OF DOOMED HOSPITAL PATIENTS ARE USED AS GUINEA PIGS FOR THEIR EXPERIMENTS. THE HOMICIDAL ITALIAN DUO ARE SAID TO HAVE CAUSED THE DEATHS OF ONE HUNDRED AND FIFTY PEOPLE IN ROME.

MATHIEU ORFILA AND THE LAFARGE MURDER

In 1840, a notorious murder trial in France puts the science of toxicology—then in its relative infancy—to the test. Marie Lafarge is charged with poisoning her husband Charles with arsenic. The prosecution introduces the findings of local doctors who performed chemical tests on Charles Lafarge's stomach and on the white powders that have been gathered as evidence.

Mathieu Orfila, the eminent professor of forensic medicine, and the world's greatest expert on toxicology, is summoned from Paris. Orfila conducts Marsh tests on samples taken from Charles Lafarge's body and the soil around the burial site. He finds definite traces of arsenic in the body, and readily demonstrates that it did not come from the surrounding soil.

GRAHAM YOUNG AND THALLIUM

On November 21, 1971, police in England pay Graham Frederick Young a visit. His coworkers had been becoming increasingly ill and two had already died. At first the mysterious illness from which each man had suffered baffles the authorities but Young, unable to resist bragging about his achievements in the field of toxicology and in particular the art of poisoning, slips up and reveals his hand. When he is arrested a lethal dose of thallium found in his pocket incriminates him. Traces of the poison are also found in both deceased victims. In July 1972 Young is found guilty of murder and sentenced to life imprisonment.

NOT RED BERRIES

On July 22, 1955, Terence Armstrong, a five-month-old baby dies at his Hampshire, U.K., home. Initial impressions are that he has consumed poisonous red berries. Subsequent postmortem analysis quickly changes this impression. The red "skins" in his stomach are actually gelatin capsules, which are found to have held the barbiturate drug Seconal. Terence's father, a naval sick bay attendant with access to just this type of drug immediately falls under suspicion. Though he denies murdering his baby son, John Armstrong is later convicted and sentenced to death at Winchester Assize Court.

DOROTHEA PUENTE'S BOARDING HOUSE

Grandmotherly Dorothea Puente runs a boarding house in California. She will become known as the Black Widow of Sacramento, as her boarders invariably end up resting under her lawn. She had been getting away with murder for years until finally she was caught and later given a life sentence in 1993.

Toxicology tests show traces of a prescription-only sleeping tablet, Dalmane (flurazepam), in all the victims' remains. Dalmane is especially potent in elderly people and can be fatal if mixed with other sedatives or alcohol. The Dalmane evidence is reinforced by her tenants' testimony.

HERMANN SANDER—THE "MERCY KILLING" CHAMPION?

In 1949 a forty-one-year-old New Hampshire, U.S., physician named Hermann Sander administers a lethal concoction of painkillers and 10cc of air to a terminally ill patient as a means of releasing her from her suffering. The worldwide acknowledged "Mercy Killing" case earns Sander celebrity status. Mrs. Abbie Borroto's cause of death is stated as "carcinoma of the large bowel with metastases."

Sander says he did not inject Mrs. Borrotto with 10cc of air while she was still alive. There is some contention over what a lethal injection of air constitutes, with the defense arguing upward of a 400cc injection and Sander is ultimately acquitted. He is viewed as an early champion of the euthanasia cause.

SWEET AUNT THALLY

In the late 1940s, four elderly members of an Australian family die. What all of these cases have in common is sixty-three-year-old Caroline Grills, who had cared for all the victims through their illnesses; her chief method of helping is endless cups of tea. A suspicious relative informs the police, who send away some of the tea for analysis. The tea is tested using the Reinsch test where it is introduced to a solution of hydrochloric acid before strips of copper are placed in the mixture. Metallic deposits on the copper prove the presence of thallium. Grills is found guilty of murder and becomes known in prison as "Aunt Thally."

MURDER BY NICOTINE

This rare murder method was used in France in the middle of the nineteenth century. It was committed by a deadly duo: Count Hippolyte Bocarmé and Lydie Fougnies. The miserable and spoilt Hippolyte marries Lydie in the hope that she would be accompanied by a large sum of money; it is not the case. The greedy partners are both sorely disappointed when Lydie's father dies poor and leaves what little he possesses to Lydie's brother Gustave. They make it their mission to invite gullible Gustave to their home, and greet him with his carefully planned death in the form of a hot drink. An internal examination of the body reveals a deadly quantity of nicotine (from the count's laboratory). The trial results in the count losing his head for the poisoning of poor Gustave.

A LETHAL FOOL

IN 1954, ARTHUR FORD ACCIDENTALLY MURDERS TWO YOUNG WOMEN WHO WORK FOR HIM WITH CANTHARIDIN (OTHERWISE KNOWN AS SPANISH FLY) FROM HIS OWN PHARMACY. FORD HEARS THAT SPANISH FLY HAS AMAZING APHRODISIAC QUALITIES AND CANNOT WAIT TO TRY IT OUT ON THESE YOUNG LADIES THAT HE SECRETLY DESIRES. WHAT HE DOES NOT REALIZE IS THAT IT WILL SLOWLY BURN THEIR INSIDES OUT. DEATH BY PASSION EARNS HIM FIVE YEARS' IMPRISONMENT, AS WELL AS BEING BRANDED A "LETHAL FOOL."

THE MERRIFIELD MURDERS

Mrs. Louisa May Merryfield is the housekeeper from hell. In 1953, she murders her own employer, but not until she has convinced Mrs. Ricketts to leave everything she owns to her in a legal will. It is only then that she feeds her a lethal treat of rat poison (phosphorus) and rum, which is later found on a spoon in her handbag. This causes an absolutely agonizing death for the innocent Mrs. Ricketts, who is left to suffer for hours before Mrs. Merryfield calls an ambulance. The forensic evidence helps to convict Louisa May Merrifield of murder, which leads to her hanging at Strangeways Prison, England.

1900s London, U.K., and Dr. Hawley Harvey Crippen, presents his mistress with some beautiful jewelry and they take a stroll together. However, a friend recognizes the jewelry as belonging to Crippen's wife, who has not been seen for a long time, and alerts the police. They discover a mutilated female body in Crippen's London home. An autopsy reveals the body is that of Mrs. Crippen, and trace amounts of hyoscine are also found, which if ingested can produce heart failure.

At this time, Crippen and his mistress are on a ship crossing the Atlantic. The captain sends a wireless message to England and Chief Inspector Dew responds by boarding the ship and arresting Crippen. The first criminal to be caught by wireless message is hanged in 1910.

THE DOCTOR WHO COULD NOT WAITE

A New York dentist named Dr. Arthur Warren Waite poisons his wife's parents with arsenic to gain her inheritance early. To hide the poison he also contaminates them with diphtheria, influenza, and tuberculosis germs.

During the autopsies, samples from the bodies are placed on a zinc plate and treated with sulphuric acid. Arsenic and hydrogen in the samples turn into a gaseous compound, and, when cooled, white crystals of arsenic oxide remain. Legitimate disease is ruled out as the cause of death and Waite is convicted of murder.

SCOPE OF FORENSIC PATHOLOGY

Forensic pathologists serve as trial experts when testifying in civil or criminal cases and are also known as forensic medical examiners and police surgeons. They perform autopsies to determine cause of death. They will determine if a person has drowned, been asphyxiated, shot, or stabbed, and decide if a death has been caused by an accident, natural causes, or homicide.

TISSUE TALES

By examining wound tissue specimens that may be relevant to sexual or other crimes, much can be told. Forensic pathologists also work closely with medical examiners. The examination of dead bodies—autopsy or postmortem—is a subset of anatomical pathology.

THE AUTOPSY

AUTOPSY OR POSTMORTEM EXAMINATION IS ONE OF THE FIRST SCIENTIFIC MEANS EMPLOYED IN THE INVESTIGATION OF SUSPICIOUS OR VIOLENT DEATH. IT REMAINS AT THE CORE OF FORENSIC MEDICINE. THE EXAMINATION INVOLVES FIRST THE INSPECTION OF THE SURFACE OF THE BODY. THIS IS THEN OPENED UP AND AFTER SURVEILLANCE OF THE BODY CAVITIES, SAMPLES ARE REMOVED FOR TOXICOLOGICAL ANALYSIS AND MICROSCOPIC INSPECTION. A REPORT IS THEN COMPILED WHICH UNDERTAKES TO RECONSTRUCT THE REASON, METHOD, AND MECHANISM OF DEATH.

THE VIRTOPSY

Switzerland's University of Berne's Institute of Forensic Medicine, in collaboration with its Institute of Diagnostic Radiology, has performed one hundred "virtual" autopsies (Virtopsy) over the last few years.

Virtual autopsy combines computed tomography (CT) and magnetic resonance (MR) imaging. The CT images provide data on the pathology of the body, generating detailed information about trauma injuries. In determining time of death, Virtopsy uses MR spectroscopy. This is a technique that measures metabolites in the brain which emerge in postmortem decomposition. MR imaging focuses on specific areas of the body, such as soft tissue, muscles, and organs.

DROWNING

The victim inhales water and chokes and this will result in the speedy creation of thick, foamy mucus in the throat and windpipe. This foam is instrumental in stopping the victim from breathing and is perceived as a "foam cone" covering the nostrils and mouth.

TO LIVE OR DIATOM

An autopsy of a body found in water will reveal whether the person was alive or dead when he/she entered the water. In all water that contains normal biosystems (oceans, rivers, etc.), tiny organisms known as diatoms exist. If the victim is alive while in the water, he will inhale these diatoms into the lungs along with the water that drowns he/she.

When, during autopsy, sections of internal organs are dissolved in strong acids, the silica shells of the diatoms remain and can then be identified under a microscope. If there are few or no diatoms present in the internal organs, the victim was most probably dead when the body entered the water.

DEATH BY DROWNING

Drowning is not as simple as it may seem; there are four main ways in which a human can be killed by water.

• Wet drowning: a mixture of air and water comes up from the lungs to fill the nostrils and mouth, suffocating the victim.

• Vagal inhibition: water enters the nose and causes spasm of the larynx to press the vagus nerve and stop the heart.

• Shock: sudden exposure to very cold water can result in an instant heart attack.

• Hypothermia: can be caused by prolonged immersion in cold water; this can result in a drop in the body's core temperature, which is followed by unconsciousness and eventually death.

ASPHYXIA

This occurs when there are insufficient quantities of oxygen reaching the brain or other vital organs. Common methods in homicides are drowning, smothering, or strangulation. In many cases where a victim has been murdered, a combination of the above will be seen, depending on how much of a struggle the victim has put up or, in some extreme cases, the killer will decide to experiment by varying his method of murder.

"BURKING"

The infamous nineteenth-century murderers, Burke and Hare, aka "The Body Snatchers," earn their living by murdering locals in Edinburgh, Scotland, and selling their bodies to teaching hospitals for anatomy study. It is vital that the cadavers show no external signs of violence and the bodies must be in prime condition. While Hare holds the intoxicated victim down, Burke kneels on the victim's chest and covers the mouth and nose, asphyxiating him. Cause of death often appears to be a heart attack or seizure. They don't get away with it forever, however, and the homicidal duo's destiny is to swing from the hangman's noose.

This process of dispatching a victim is known today as "Burking," to police and criminals alike.

STRANGULATION: THE HANDS-ON APPROACH
Strangulation can be accidental, suicidal, or homicidal. The latter is usually achieved either manually—by violent choking with hands around a victim's neck—or by ligature, (e.g., garrote, wire or rope). All strangulations are characterized by cyanosis, enlarged and engorged veins, and intensive heart congestion. Many sadistic murderers favour this method of killing their victim as it allows them to control their hapless victim's breathing. They will often experiment by choking them as close to the brink of death as they dare before releasing the pressure and reviving them briefly, only to commence the horrible ritual once more.

MURDER BY LIGATURE

An assailant places a ligature around his victim's neck and tightens it in order to silence, control, and/or kill. Examples of ligature include belts, necklaces, electrical cords, stockings, metal wires, ropes, scarves, ties, etc. The cause of death is the obstruction of vessels supplying blood and oxygen to the brain. Loss of consciousness is estimated to occur after ten to fifteen seconds. In particularly brutal acts of strangulation, separation of the vertebrae can occur, tearing the spinal cord and causing instant death.

SIGNS OF TRAUMA—PETECHIAE

In cases of ligature strangulation, it's easy to identify physical evidence of traumatic asphyxia. Often visible are petechiae; veins are usually at a lower pressure than arteries, therefore traumatic injuries caused by ligature strangulation result in an increase in capillary pressure which results in damage to the capillaries.

This damage is illustrated by tiny points of bleeding in the soft tissues. These pinpoint hemorrhages are known as "petechiae." Other less common evidence is blood issuing from the victim's mouth or nose. However, if this is not present it is not an indication that ligature strangulation has not taken place. The hands of the victim should be looked at carefully as they often clutch at the hair of their attacker.

A SECOND OPINION

Following the examination the body of a thirty-three-year-old man lying face down on a track, the consensus of opinion at the police mortuary is that he had died suddenly of natural causes. However, it is routine to refer the body to the medical examiner and in this case he has plenty to say.

Although no injury to the neck is obvious, dissection reveals bruising. There are red petechiae covering the eyelids and conjunctivae and further mucosal pinpoints of bleeding on the walls of the epiglottis and oropharynx. Dissection of the back demonstrates fresh bruising within the muscles and there is a section of hemorrhage 8mm in dimension on the side of the tongue. The cause of death is given as strangulation.

ANSWERS FROM WOUNDS

Forensic pathologists use wound analysis in their efforts to reconstruct what happened between a victim and his/her assailant. They need to learn if the wound occurred ante- or postmortem. There are many types of wounds including; stab wounds, blunt force wounds, rape wounds, bullet wounds, and burn wounds.

TEMPERATURE DROP

In cases of suspicious death, a pathologist or anthropologist is called to the scene to establish a time of death. This is achieved by taking the corpse's internal body temperature. Measurable changes occur after death as the body slowly begins to cool. A body's normal temperature level is approximately 98.6°F and will drop at a rate of one half to two degrees per hour for the initial twelve hours after death. These circumstances are dependent on factors such as the victim's build, clothing, etc. In the following twelve-hour period, the body temperature will drop by around half the rate.

RIGOR MORTIS

A LATIN TERM TRANSLATING AS "THE STIFFNESS OF DEATH," RIGOR MORTIS COMMENCES FOLLOWING A BODY'S INTERNAL CHEMISTRY CHANGE FROM ITS NORMAL ACID STATE TO AN ALKALINE STATE. THIS PROCESS TAKES APPROXIMATELY TWO HOURS AFTER A PERSON DIES. MUSCLES THAT WERE RELAXED PRIOR TO LIFE BEING EXTINGUISHED WILL GROW TENSE AND BEGIN TO STIFFEN, BEGINNING WITH THE EYELIDS, FACE, AND JAW, AND PROGRESSING DOWN THE BODY, THROUGHOUT THE ARMS AND TRUNK, AND CULMINATING IN THE LEGS. RIGOR MORTIS IS COMPLETE OVER A TWELVE-HOUR PERIOD AND CAN BE PRESENT FOR UP TO FORTY-EIGHT HOURS.

LIVOR MORTIS

"The bruising of death" that is livor mortis aids when investigators are trying to establish a time of death. Red blood cells will descend via force of gravity to areas throughout the body in contact with the ground, when the heart stops beating and circulation ceases. The results are a bruised color present within two hours of death. If the body is left sedentary this coloration remains as more red cells are broken down and separated into muscle tissue. If a poison has been ingested by the victim, such bruising can appear quite vivid. An example is carbon monoxide poisoning, which results in bright red coloring in the lower parts of the body.

THE CADAVERIC SPASM

Similar to the symptoms of rigor mortis, the cadaveric spasm occurs at the very moment of a violent death. Anything that the victim may be gripping can be held in a vicelike grip for several hours. Although at first it is impossible to loosen the muscles from the spasm, the muscles relax as regular rigor mortis takes hold of the corpse. Investigators have sometimes been lucky enough to find the hair, skin samples, or clothing fibers of the perpetrator in the victim's grasp.

BREAKDOWN

When a body is discovered after an extended period of time after death, decomposition can give pointers as to the length of time the corpse has been undiscovered. Bacteria will break down blood cells, and after two days produce green staining along the flanks of the abdomen. More staining will appear over the following two days and the neck and trunk will swell. After seven days, blistering will also appear on the skin's surface.

MORE ON BLOOD POOLING

The pooling of blood is a crucial indication of the time of death. It is referred to as "hypostasis." This happens because the blood stops flowing and settles in the lower parts of the body. The skin then turns pink or red. The process occurs up to six hours after death.

COLOR OF THE SKIN

From forty-eight hours and onwards the color of the corpse will help to indicate the time of death. At this point the skin acquires a greenish tint, as bacteria will have begun to breed. The color change begins in the lower abdomen and spreads outward, leaving the feet and hands the last affected. Thereafter, between four and seven days after death, the skin will assume a marble-like, blue-veined appearance.

THE EYES

When a person dies his/her eyes will remain as they were at the exact moment he lost his/her life. Because there is less fluid pressure behind them, the eyeballs will become softer, and within three hours of death a cloudy film will appear over the eyes.

Literally translated from the Greek as meaning "absence of pulse," the term asphyxia is thought by some pathologists to be equivocal. In the broadest terms it means a state in which the body has an excess of carbon dioxide and is deprived of oxygen (hypercapnia and hypoxia). The end result is loss of consciousness and/or death.

Asphyxial deaths are caused by:

- Airway obstruction
- Lack of oxygen
- Chest compression
- Neck compression
- Positional/postural asphyxia

"CUSTODY DEATH SYNDROME"

Prisoners who die while in police custody usually provoke the accusation of police brutality, followed by lawsuits and public outrage. Investigators have reached the conclusion that many fatalities are due to multiple causes, including the stress that goes hand in hand with police confrontation, drug abuse, and occasionally restraint or "hog-tying" (the restricting of a person's hands and feet by way of securing them together) of prisoners who are already distressed. Sudden death that ensues from violent struggles with police has been called "Custody Death Syndrome."

"EXCITED DELIRIUM"

A struggling suspect from San Francisco is being transported to the police station. Having been restrained, he is put in the back of a police wagon. He is dead before he arrives at the station.

The medical examiner maintains his death was caused by "excited delirium." Police worldwide are learning to look out for the warning signs of this fairly recent phenomenon. "Sudden deaths are not new, but the concept of a 'syndrome' is an emerging idea. We are just starting to recognize it," says Forensics Group, Inc. Principal Neil Zinn.

The suspect's family sued the San Francisco Police Department for ten million dollars, citing police brutality.

OLDER THAN THEY LOOK

THE PHENOMENON OF "EXCITED DELIRIUM" IS KNOWN OF IN 1989 BUT IT ISN'T UNTIL 1992 THAT THE SAN DIEGO POLICE DEPARTMENT PUBLISH A CRITICAL STUDY ON "EXCITED DELIRIUM," "POSITIONAL ASPHYXIA," AND DRUG OVERDOSE. ON THE OCCASIONS DESCRIBED, SUSPECTS ARE SUPPOSED TO HAVE SUFFOCATED WHILE RESTRAINED AND PLACED FACE DOWN. ACCORDING TO PATHOLOGISTS IT IS STILL EXTREMELY RARE FOR PEOPLE TO SUDDENLY DIE EVEN IN SUCH SITUATIONS. DR. JOHN CLARK, CHIEF MEDICAL OFFICER FOR THE LOS ANGELES SHERIFF'S DEPARTMENT, SAYS, "CLEARLY THIS IS [THE RESULT OF] A COMBINATION OF FACTORS INCLUDING SUBSTANCE ABUSE,

EXTREME AGITATION, AND POOR PHYSICAL SHAPE…AND [MANY] ARE MEDICALLY OLDER THAN THEIR STATED AGE— A FORTY-YEAR-OLD WILL HAVE THE BODY OF A FIFTY-FIVE- OR SIXTY-YEAR-OLD DUE TO SUBSTANCE AND DRUG ABUSE."

UNUSUAL BEHAVIOR

Because of the emergence of "Custody Death Syndrome," police authorities are reviewing the manner in which their officers restrain violent suspects. These deaths usually occur when police are called to a scene where the suspect is acting weirdly and causing a commotion.

More often than not they are high on drugs. They tend to get hysterical and act violently. Sometimes the suspect is in a frenzy and sweating profusely, or has removed all his clothes—obesity appears to be another risk factor.

Typically the suspect is subdued and restrained but abruptly, when the situation appears under control, the suspect ceases to breathe and dies. Even if commenced immediately all resuscitation attempts fail. The autopsy usually cannot find a clear cause of death.

EVIDENCE EVIDENCE EVIDENCE
EVIDENCE EVIDENCE EVIDENCE
EVIDENCE EVIDENCE EVIDENCE

Traces of Evidence

"With contact between two items, there will be an exchange."
Locard's Principle

THE EXCHANGE PRINCIPLE

In the 1900s Dr. Edmond Locard announces his "Exchange Principle." The theory behind this concept is that every person involved in a crime leaves some trace behind them and often takes something away with them. This principle pioneers the development of forensic science. There are many types of trace evidence including hair, fibers, and dirt. Trace evidence alone is seldom enough to prove guilt but it is often used to corroborate other pertinent case evidence.

SWEET JUSTICE

When taking part in a tense criminal activity, an individual might calm himself by chewing a piece of gum or smoking a cigarette. If that individual then throws away that sweet paper or that cigarette end at or close to the crime scene he has cooked his own goose. A sticky sweet paper can attract fibers and hairs, sometimes allowing forensic scientists to match those found at the scene with others found on the suspect's clothing or body. Cells of saliva gathered from a piece of gum or cigarette end can provide sufficient DNA for a profile of the offender and connect him to the scene of the crime.

The transfer of hairs can occur when there is physical contact. If the transfer takes place from the area of the body in which they are growing this is a "primary transfer." If they transfer from an individual's clothing this is referred to as a "secondary transfer." Every day each person is thought to shed about a hundred head hairs—on to items in the environment and on to clothing. Contact between a suspect's environment and a victim results in a secondary transfer and is a common means of evidentiary advancement to the solving of a case.

DETERMINATION OF BODY AREA

THE CURLINESS, COLOR, LENGTH, STIFFNESS, SHAPE, AND MICROSCOPIC APPEARANCE OF HAIR ARE ALL CONDUCIVE TO THE DETERMINATION OF BODY AREA. SOFTNESS AND COLOR ALSO HELP IDENTIFY BODY AREA. UNDER THE MICROSCOPE, HAIRS THAT SHARE DIFFERENT ANATOMICAL REGIONS ARE CALLED BODY HAIRS. THESE ARE TYPICALLY HAIRS LOCATED ON THE BACK, LOWER ABDOMEN, AND UPPER LEGS. THERE IS GREAT VARIATION IN PUBIC AND HEAD HAIRS AND THIS HAS LED TO MOST FORENSIC WORK BEING CONCENTRATED ON THE COMPARISON OF HAIRS FROM THE PUBIC AREA AND THE HEAD.

THE DEFILING OF THE QUEEN'S HEAD

One of the main principles of forensic science could not be better illustrated than by the fact that over half of all five pound notes in circulation within the UK are believed to be contaminated with cocaine. Miniscule traces of the drug are passed from hand to note and from note to hand. The same principle is applied to allow forensic scientists to create links between suspects and crime scenes. It also demonstrates the astonishing power of modern methods of chemical analysis. Gas Chromatography combined with Mass Spectroscopy (GM-MS) can detect traces as little as 3.5 one hundred million millionth of an ounce of cocaine.

NEVILLE HEATH MEETS HIS MAKER

On July 3, 1946, a man named Neville Heath is busy entertaining Miss Doreen Marshall over dinner at the West Cliff Hotel, Bournemouth, England. The pair head off into the night at approximately 11:30 p.m. Doreen Marshall is never again seen alive. Horribly murdered and mutilated, her body is discovered the next day and the hunt is on for her missing companion. Finding Heath's left luggage, police open his suitcase and, among other items, discover some blood-stained clothing with some hairs attached. These are later matched with an earlier murder victim named Margery Gardner. There is also a heavily bloodstained riding switch. This forensic evidence leads Heath to the gallows where his final request to notorious hangman Albert Pierrepoint is for a glass of whisky. Briefly thinking it over Heath says: "I think I'll make it a double."

THE VELCRO STRAP THAT HELD A KILLER

In the year 2000, the body of eight-year-old Sarah Payne is discovered badly decomposed after a massive media-encouraged manhunt. Police are struggling to produce evidence linking a suspect, so they enlist the help of the Forensic Science Service (FSS).

Of particular interest is a Velcro strap on one of Sarah's shoes that holds three hundred fibers. Under a low-power microscope, dark red fibers are discovered. The fibers match a red sweatshirt which is found in the van of Roy Whiting.

When Whiting's jumper is examined by the FSS under a high-power microscope, they find a few blond hairs. More hairs are found in his van along with some green fibers. When tested, the hairs match Sarah's DNA profile and the green fibers are identified as from the green dress she was wearing when she disappeared. The tiny fibers cause Whiting to be arrested.

• More than twenty forensic experts were involved from the fields of pathology, archaeology, oil/lubricant analysis, entomology, geology, and environmental profiling.

• Over five hundred items were sent for forensic analysis.

• Overall the investigation cost in excess of three-and-a-half million US dollars and involved a thousand people.

I'M A LUMBERJACK BUT NOT OK

After a failed robbery on a mail train in Southern Oregon, in which the train was blown up with dynamite and the crew slaughtered, the police have little evidence other than some sacking shoe covers and a pair of overalls. Dr. Edward Heinrich of Berkeley, California, intensely studies the overalls under a powerful microscope and yields incredible results.

Fir tree oil and chippings are found in the pockets of the overalls, the left-hand pockets show more wear than the right and the garment is buttoned from the left. A brown hair is found among tobacco strands.

From this Heinrich announces that police should hunt for a left-handed lumberjack at five-foot-ten inches tall and in his early twenties, who has light brown hair and rolls his own cigarettes. He would be from the Pacific Northwest.

Roy d'Autremont fits the bill perfectly and he, along with his two brothers, has not been seen since the robbery. Eventually found using fake names, all three brothers confess and are convicted.

THE ATLANTA CHILD MURDERER— CAUGHT BY CARPET

Between 1979 and 1981, Wayne Williams, convicted of the appalling "Atlanta Child Murders" strangles more than twenty young men and boys to death, leaving behind little evidence.

However one piece of evidence proves to be Williams's downfall. An unusual green fiber is found on the clothing of some of his victims. The fibers are traced to an olive green carpet manufactured in Dalton, Georgia, and only 17,932 square yards were ever produced.

Williams bought this carpet for his house and the left-over pieces were used to carpet his automobile. Experts predict that the chances of anyone else having this particular carpet in their house and vehicle are one in thirty million. Williams is convicted and sentenced to two life terms in prison.

TYPING AND DETERMINING: PAINT

In vehicular crimes, vandalism, and those crimes that involve forced entry, paint can often aid in forensic detection. Most commonly analyzed paint types compared at the Forensic Laboratory are architectural, aerosol, and automotive.

By analyzing a single microscopic paint chip the make, model, year, and even the manufacturing plant of an evading vehicle can be determined.

The Laboratory works with the Federal Bureau of Investigation and Royal Canadian Mounted Police Automotive Paint Database (APD). The database contains more than forty-four thousand automotive paint types from the 1960s to present-day vehicles. The APD provides investigative leads to agencies trying to locate hit-and-run case suspects.

PAINTING A PICTURE

There are no witnesses to a crash which leaves an automobile turned upside down on its roof with one passenger dead and the other seriously injured. Among other evidence such as a piece of license plate in the exhaust, investigators find some large, gray metallic chips of paint in the road. Back at the laboratory and under the microscope, the paint chips are found to be of an unusual metallic color, typical of older Pontiac vehicles. This leads rapidly to the seizure of a suspect vehicle. Because the paint chips are substantial, physical matching is possible and three pieces are easily fitted to the vehicle making analysis of the paint unnecessary.

LIGHT BULBS: HOT WHEN ILLUMINATED

Vehicle headlights, turn signals, and rear lights may yield clues as to what happened by way of their light bulbs. These may be analyzed in ascertaining whether the bulb was on or off during a motor accident. The filament within the bulb rapidly heats up when illuminated. If a vehicle is involved in a collision the original coil shape is deformed by metal softening under the intense heat afforded by rapid deceleration and centrifugal forces. If the bulb breaks small fragments of glass will scatter across the hot filament and melt, and the rapid addition of oxygen into the bulb will cause oxidation of the tungsten filament. A laboratory examination will conclude that the filament was hot and thus the light was on at the moment of collision if any of these conditions are found.

GREEN FIBERS NAIL THE SUSPECT

The body of a young girl is found by a police dog in 1998 in Connecticut. Her throat has been cut and she has a blunt instrument injury to the left side of her head. Using alternate light sources, scientists find fibers in the victim's hair. In the laboratory two types of fiber are isolated— beige carpet and bright green acrylic. One suspect lives in a building close to the crime scene. Although bleached, the suspect's jeans reveal tiny bloodstains but these are not sufficient for DNA analysis. Trace evidence from the jeans also finds beige and green fibers. A blanket owned by the suspect is the origin of the green fibers. He is convicted and sentenced to life in prison.

On December 21, 1988, Pan Am Flight 103 falls from the skies while en route to New York. All two hundred and fifty-nine passengers are killed, as well as eleven people from the small Scottish village of Lockerbie, where most of the debris falls. The crash measures 1.6 on the Richter scale; twenty-one houses in Lockerbie are destroyed and debris scatters over northern England and southern Scotland.

The fact that no distress call is made, the scatter of the parts, and the fact that autopsies reveal that victims suffer massive lung damage from violent decompression lead investigators to believe the plane exploded in the air. They find among the debris parts of a cassette player that contain fragments of Semtex and clothing fibers.

It was a bomb. Investigators manage to trace the fibers to specific articles of clothing bought in Malta and then shipped to Frankfurt, Germany on the day of the crash. The clothes were bought by a Libyan, who did not board the plane. Libya eventually admits to the terrorist strike and airport security changes policy on baggage-loading as a result.

TAPE FOR BINDING

Tape is often used to bind victims and to seal letters, packages, and explosives. Specific information as to the manufacturer of the tape may be yielded from glue and backing. Fabric reinforcement is another tape component and can narrow down a certain batch of tape to be used as a comparison sample.

As other trace materials also adhere to tape, there will often be an abundance of evidence. The tape's edge can also be used to determine certain physical matches.

TOOL MARKS: A THIEF'S STOCK IN TRADE

A new tool, besides acquiring traces of substances it comes into contact with, incurs minute chips and nicks that cause its edges and blades to become unique. Tool marks are most frequently discovered at burglary locations involving filing cabinets, window sills, cash registers, window frames, doors, and door frames. A thief, professional or otherwise, will have to tread very carefully indeed to successfully avoid all of these areas during the commission of his crime.

THE CARPET FITTER

In 2000, police are investigating the kidnapping and sexual assault of young girls. Their chief suspect is a carpet fitter. The victims' clothing, the assault evidence collection kits, the suspect's vehicle, and other clothing evidence are all conveyed to the laboratory for analysis. Many carpet-type fibers of various colors are examined under the microscope and deemed to be similar by comparison. A semen stain on a victim's T-shirt is found to match the suspect's DNA profile. When confronted with the evidence, the accused confesses. Among other charges are two counts of sexual assault in the first degree and thirty-two counts of kidnapping in the first degree. He is now serving thirty-eight years with no possibility of parole.

GLASS: A TELLTALE CRIME SCENE INDICATOR

When there is a lack of other physical evidence to match and substantiate, glass fragments at a crime scene—most commonly a house break-in, vehicular theft, or drive-by homicide—may be analyzed to determine whether or not the known and questioned samples could have a common origin.

When a particular fragment of glass, such as a headlight or window fragment, is analyzed at the laboratory, the examiners are able to identify the type of glass and successfully isolate possible original sources.

ALL OVER THE PLACE

Fibers are everywhere. As such they are transferred in nearly all types of crime: on a murder victim during a struggle with her attacker or a sexual assault being made upon her, attached to the blade of a knife, nestled in the trunk of a vehicle used to transport either a dead body or a kidnap victim, or perhaps on a window sill at the scene of a burglary. So tiny are most fibers that they are often invisible to the untrained eye and are frequently missed by even the most thorough and dedicated of offenders during the course of their crime commission.

IDENTIFYING RESTRAINTS

Many assailants, having preplanned their crime, will bring along with them some item or items with which to bind their victim in order to control them. They may also elect to fashion restraints from items of clothing or belongings of the victim.

Ropes and cordage such as tape and handcuffs are common evidential items to take into consideration when a victim has been restrained, and subtle composition differences in cordage construction are readily identified by a fiber examiner.

FABRIC DAMAGE

Typically in a murder or rape cases where some form of violence has been used—so most—damage caused to a fabric is examined when attempting to ascertain whether it was cut or ripped.

This type of examination may be critical in the reconstruction of an assault as it can sometimes determine that an alleged attack never occurred, an obviously important factor to consider in verifying suspicious or bogus claims made by an alleged or self-proclaimed victim.

FIBER ANALYSTS

Much of the work of the fiber analyst is the analysis of trace evidence of a very specialized type.

Fibers are placed into four broad categories:
- Synthetics (e.g., acrylic, rayon, nylon, acetate, polyester, and olefin)
- Plant (e.g., cotton, hemp, sisal)
- Animal (e.g., wool, fur, silk)
- Mineral (e.g., asbestos)

There are many thousands of types of synthetic materials and chemical techniques that are employed to discover the precise nature of the organic compounds present.

Scientists can study a fiber's shape by using an assortment of microscopes—even the manner in which a fiber has worn or faded can yield important clues. Extra data on a fiber's properties can be achieved with the use of special viewing techniques like fluorescent microscopy or polarized light. If it is detected that a fiber has been coated, for example, by mud or blood, and the substance is analyzed, this can also provide important information.

TAKING A CLOSER LOOK

The examination of fibers:
Initially the fiber is placed under a microscope to ascertain the type, e.g., wool, cotton. Then it is examined for colors and the width of the fiber is measured. Does it contain any "delustrant?" Manufacturers use this in varying degrees to decide how shiny the garment is to be.

MICROSPECTROPHOTOMETRY

A microspectrophotomete sends a beam of light through the fiber, thereby enabling a computer to obtain the components of color. The color can be extracted if the fiber is big enough, and a thin-layer chromatography test performed to determine the dyes that give the fiber its color. If it is a man-made fiber an infra-red spectrophotometry, a chemical analysis, is performed to determine if the fiber is made of, e.g., acrylic, nylon, polyester.

FINGERNAIL CLIPPINGS

Fingernail clippings are usually collected by the medical examiner. Under furious assault the victim may have scratched the attacker while attempting to defend himself from the onslaught and the assailant's skin may therefore be present under the victim's nails. It is a rarity but in some cases examination unearths not only tissue beneath the fingernails but enough for comprehensive DNA analysis.

TWO LOST GIRLS AND THEIR FOOTBALL SHIRTS

TWO TEN-YEAR-OLD GIRLS NAMED JESSICA CHAPMAN AND HOLLY WELLS DISAPPEAR FROM HOLLY'S HOME IN SOHAM, CAMBRIDGESHIRE, ENGLAND, IN AUGUST 2002. THIRTEEN DAYS LATER THE SEARCH IS CALLED OFF WHEN THE GIRLS' BODIES ARE FOUND IN MILDENHALL, SUFFOLK.

FROM VARIOUS SCENES, INCLUDING THE HOME OF PRIME SUSPECT IAN HUNTLEY, THE FSS ARE ABLE TO RETRIEVE SUBSTANTIAL AMOUNTS OF EVIDENCE.

OVER A FOURTEEN-MONTH PERIOD OF WORKING AROUND THE CLOCK, SCIENTISTS ARE ABLE TO LINK HAIRS FROM HUNTLEY AND FIBERS FROM HIS CLOTHES AND HOUSE TO THE MANCHESTER UNITED FOOTBALL SHIRTS WORN BY THE GIRLS WHEN LAST SEEN. FORTY THOUSAND FIBERS ARE EXAMINED, AND THE FSS PROVIDE EVIDENCE OF A TWO-WAY TRANSFER OF ONE HUNDRED AND FIFTY-FOUR FIBERS BETWEEN HUNTLEY'S CARPETS AND CLOTHING AND THE TRACKSUIT BOTTOMS AND FOOTBALL SHIRTS OF THE TWO GIRLS.

IAN HUNTLEY IS CONVICTED OF THE MURDERS OF JESSICA CHAPMAN AND HOLLY WELLS IN DECEMBER 2003 AT THE OLD BAILEY. HE IS SENT TO PRISON FOR LIFE.

HUMAN OR ANIMAL?

A common application of hair analysis is in determining whether the hair in question is of human or animal origin. This can be established by comparing the scale patterns of the cuticle and the medullary index. The medullary index is the ratio of medulla to shaft size. The human ratio is usually under one third. The shape and the pattern of the medulla will also indicate whether a hair is human or animal. From this an investigator will also know what species of animal the hair came from.

HAIR: WHAT ARE THE CHANCES?

A wealth of information can be provided from a single hair; however, it is not admissible as evidence alone, but only in conjunction with other findings. Hair is often used to support other evidence and is more a matter of probabilities. With a strand of hair from a victim found on a suspect there is around a one in eight hundred chance that this happened by accident. And if a hair from the suspect is also found somewhere on or near the victim, the probability of an accidental transfer increases to one in 640,000.

Although hair from other parts of the body can be used, it is head hairs that are best when an examiner is tasked with determining race. Forensic scientists are able to make a distinction between hairs of Caucasoid (European ancestry), Negroid (African ancestry), and Mongoloid (Asian ancestry) because of microscopic characteristics which are different from one racial group to another. It can be a problem when hair from persons from mixed racial ancestry are involved because they may have microscopic characteristics from more than one racial group.

LOOKING FOR THE PREVIOUS OWNER

In Toronto, a small boy out riding his bicycle is hit by an automobile. The boy receives serious head wounds but the driver fails to stop and there are no eye witnesses to the incident.

Three years later police are undertaking an inspection of local scrapyards to see if any of the vehicles may have been involved in crimes. This is a routine check and samples are taken from a Chrysler Coronet. Forensics match these to paint fragments removed from the clothing of the young boy involved in the earlier hit-and-run case. Investigators are also able to trace the previous owner of the car and the man is charged and found guilty of criminal negligence, causing bodily harm, and failing to remain at the scene of an accident.

Peter Sutcliffe, perhaps better known by his well deserved press-dubbed moniker of "The Yorkshire Ripper," has been successfully murdering women throughout the 1970s and the police are still no closer to catching him. That is until he makes a small mistake that leads to his capture. In October 1977, Sutcliffe picks up Jean Jordan, a twenty-year-old prostitute from Manchester. When she gets into his car he pays her and she places the money in her handbag.

Shortly after the transaction Jean is dead and Sutcliffe dumps her bag in a hedge nearly two hundred yards from her body. Unfortunately for Sutcliffe, he pays her with a brand new "fiver" (five pound note)—one that can be traced back to his employers, and subsequently Sutcliffe himself. It is this evidence that finally links him indisputably to the Ripper murders.

THE GREEN BULLDOG

A fifteen-year-old girl named Jenna Baldwin disappears from her home in September, 2002, but her stepfather, Mike Baldwin, reassures family and friends that she is fine. Police are suspicious of this casual dismissal and arrest him. He subsequently tells them he panicked after Jenna had fallen down the stairs after an argument, and she had died in his automobile on the way to hospital. Investigators know that Baldwin had purchased a green "Bulldog" brand of shovel a day after Jenna's disappearance, but Baldwin denies using it to bury her, saying instead that he had used an old, rusty shovel and his bare hands.

There are two sites for the burial—the first Baldwin discards because of stones and plant roots. But scientists examine the soil, stones and roots from both areas, finding green paint smears which match the type found on the shovel. Mike Baldwin is jailed for life in 2003.

CHEMISTRY AND RADIOCARBON DATING

Willard Libby, Professor of Chemistry at the University of Chicago, is awarded the 1960 Nobel Prize for Chemistry in recognition of his groundbreaking work in the field of radiocarbon dating. In conjunction with hydrogen, non-metallic element carbon (C) occurs as an organic compound component found largely in the earth, in the form of carbonates like chalk and limestone and in the air, as carbon dioxide. In plants it is cellulose and in animals, starch and sugar. As a consequence the radiocarbon method is suitable for dating organic matter, such as determining when a person died.

COMPOUND MICROSCOPE
The basic microscope that uses two lenses (or a combination of lenses), an objective lens and an eyepiece lens, to focus a greatly magnified image of the subject on the retina of the observer's eye.

DENSITY GRADIENT TUBE
Equipment for measuring the distribution of particles of different density in a soil sample by determining the point at which they are suspended in a glass tube filled with successive layers of liquid of differing densities.

ELECTRON MICROSCOPE
This is a microscope that forms its image by the electrons emitted from the specimen, when scanned by a focused beam of electrons.

GAS CHROMATOGRAPHY
Gas chromatography is a technique for separating complex mixtures of substances according to their movement when carried by gas through a film of liquid.

MASS SPECTROMETRY

Mass spectrometry is a way of identifying the constituent parts of a mixture by passing their molecules through a high vacuum chamber, where they acquire a positive charge through colliding with a beam of electrons that separates them according to their different masses.

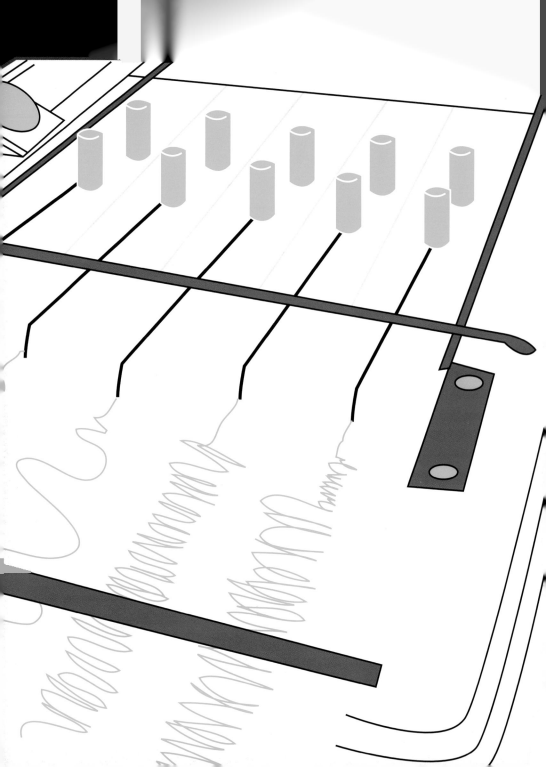

The Psychological Perspective

"I have been a human animile [sic] ever since I was born."

Serial killer, Carl Panzram

A HISTORY IN PROFILE

In the Middle Ages the advent of profiling is first seen. Inquisitors first attempt to profile heretics. In the 1800s it is the turn of Jacob Fries, Cesare Lombroso, Alphonse Bertillon, and Hans Gross to realize the potential of this powerful tool. A lot of their research, however, is considered to be prejudiced—a hallmark of the biases of their time.

PHYSIOGNOMY: ASSESSING THE CRIMINAL

The system of divination by use of physiognomy evolves much later than would be expected considering that human beings have been intuitively gauging one another.

Physiognomy is an early prototype of an investigatory means of identifying and anticipating a suspected person's criminal disposition. Whereas now an investigator will apply criminal profiling or use specialized psychological and investigative tools to determine a suspect's character, in the late seventeenth century a criminal's personality and psychological makeup is said to be demonstrable by the structure of his face. After much development the concept is still a burgeoning and constantly evolving science and character assessment continues to play an important role in crime detection.

CRIMINAL PROFILING

"Offender profiling," also known as criminal profiling, criminal personality profiling, criminological profiling, behavioral profiling, or criminal investigative analysis has a more scientific term, "psychological profiling." This is a behavioral and investigative tool harnessed by investigators to profile an unknown subject.

Psychological profiling is considered the "third wave" of investigative science in modern criminology circles and despite its predominant U.S. associations, was actually pioneered by Scotland Yard in the nineteeth century. It involves the study of crime itself in conjunction with the study of the abnormal psyche of the criminal perpetrator.

THE CRIME SCENE ANALYST AND THE PROFILER

There is an argument that sees a difference between a crime scene analyst and a profiler. A person familiar with police methods (crime scene analyst) can analyze the M.O. of a criminal but only a profiler can analyse the "signature." The signature is what the offender does that is removed from the commission of the crime itself—for example, unnecessary stabbing, elaborate binding of the victim, engaging in sex with the body, arranging the scene, etc. For some murderers it is not sufficient simply to kill, they must in some way act out their fantasies again and again.

It is this unique characteristic of the criminal's personality that is his signature, and if investigators need to discover whether two or more crimes are committed by the same perpetrator, they must concentrate on this.

QUANTICO

FORENSIC PROFILERS ASSIST PROSECUTORS, DEFENDERS, AND LAW ENFORCEMENT INVESTIGATORS IN UNDERSTANDING A RANGE OF NORMAL AND CRIMINAL BEHAVIORS, SOMETIMES SERVING AS "CRIMINAL PROFILERS." FAMOUS EXAMPLES ARE THOSE PROFILERS OF THE BEHAVIORAL SCIENCE UNIT (BSU) AT QUANTICO, VIRGINIA, U.S., WHICH SO INFLUENCED THOMAS HARRIS'S NOVELS *RED DRAGON* AND *THE SILENCE OF THE LAMBS*. AMONG THE BETTER KNOWN NAMES AMONG THIS CRIMINOLOGICAL BREED ARE ROBERT RESSLER, JOHN DOUGLAS, RUSS VORPAGEL, AND ROY HAZELWOOD. ALL OF THESE CONTINUE TO EDUCATE THROUGH THEIR BIOGRAPHICAL BOOKS, TEXTBOOKS AND WEBSITES, AND TO LECTURE ON THE SUBJECT.

THE YOUNGER GENERATION

In the Juvenile Courts, psychological profilers are often asked to perform an assessment as a means of determining whether a youthful offender can be rehabilitated, what the chances of his reoffending are and what kind of supervision he will need when released back into the community.

STAGING A CRIME

Usually staging occurs for one of two reasons: to protect the victim or to lead the investigation away from the main suspect. Commonly the offender, when helping police with their inquiries, will try to direct the investigation away from himself. He will either be hysterical with grief or be helpful in the extreme. Investigators learn early on in their careers to be suspicious about someone who demonstrates such exaggerated behavior.

PROFILING STATISTICS

A murdered woman is discovered in an abandoned building. She is found with stab wounds to her abdomen and violent blunt force trauma to her head; she is bound and her face is covered by her underwear. In this situation a profile of the attacker might be developed following this rationale:

Eighty-five percent of known killers who inflict severe blunt force trauma to the facial region of their victims live with their mothers. Seventy-five percent of known killers who utilized constraints during the crime are between the ages of twenty-five to thirty-one, drive a 4x4 truck, are white and are highly intelligent.

PROFILING JACK

The first case in which the discipline of psychological profiling is used in an effort to catch a serial killer is in London, England, in 1888. A cold-blooded murderer given the nickname of "Jack the Ripper" is hunting down and slaughtering local prostitutes. George B. Phillips, a police surgeon, draws attention to the fact that each of the victims has had their organs removed with an accuracy that could only be achieved by a person trained in the medical or butchering business. Despite this, and the fact that the police receive several insolent notes signed "Jack the Ripper," the murderer goes on to kill a total of five women—with two other homicides suspected. To this day his identity remains a mystery.

In 1888, two medical doctors named George Phillips and Thomas Bond attempt to get inside the mind of Jack the Ripper, using basic profiling techniques. Dr. Bond is a police surgeon who assisted in the autopsy on Mary Kelly, the final positively known Ripper victim. He is later to become an offender-profiling pioneer. Bond notes the sexual nature of the murders and pays close attention to the inherent misogyny and fury driving the killer. He reconstructs the murder and interprets the behavior pattern of the offender: he would be a loner, middle-aged, disheveled in appearance, possibly a butcher.

THOMAS HARRIS AND
HANNIBAL THE CANNIBAL

Perhaps unsurprisingly the world of fiction has caught on to the fascinating and often sensational aspects of criminal and psychological profiling, beginning in essence with Thomas Harris's visit to Quantico and his conversations with real-life counterparts as a means to convincingly develop well known characters like Clarice Starling, Jack Crawford, and Will Graham, who battle evil murderers in his celebrated works *Red Dragon*, *The Silence of the Lambs,* and *Hannibal,* all of which revolve around the diabolical serial killer and cannibal Dr. Hannibal Lecter.

CORNWELL AND SCARPETTA

Another famous fictional crime series are the *Kay Scarpetta* books (written by Patricia Cornwell) featuring Benson Weasly, an FBI Criminal Profiler based, of course, at Quantico, Virginia. The character displays the disciplines and skills of a profiler.

THE RACE IS ON

In England in 1985, Leicester University geneticist Dr. Alec Jeffreys is approached by the West Midlands Police. They ask if he can confirm the rape confession of a seventeen-year-old boy to aid their efforts to link the youth to a second, related offence.

Comparisons of the DNA profile of the young suspect with those extracted from samples taken from victims eliminate him from the inquiry. The result is sensational and the race to bring DNA testing into the criminal justice system begins.

Popular science journals speculate on DNA profiles obtained in this way and posit that they might also be used in identifying criminals. Jeffreys is the first to put these speculations to the test.

THE RAILWAY RAPIST

In 1986, pioneering expert in "psychological profiling" Professor David Canter aids the Surrey Police in their pursuit of a serial killer dubbed "The Railway Rapist." Using a computer printout of the names of four thousand nine hundred sex offenders they are able to isolate one name, John Francis Duffy. He has earlier been charged with loitering near railway stations. Committing crimes near railway lines is part of this killer's "signature," or "mental map" as Professor Canter calls it. The case leads to the development of psychological profiling techniques in the 1980s.

THE VAMPIRE OF SACRAMENTO

SACRAMENTO, CALIFORNIA, AND ANOTHER DERANGED MURDERER IS ON THE LOOSE (NICKNAMED "THE VAMPIRE OF SACRAMENTO" BECAUSE HE DRINKS HIS VICTIMS' BLOOD). AFTER RICHARD CHASE'S THIRD HOMICIDE, FBI AGENTS ARE CALLED IN TO COMPILE A PROFILE OF THE KILLER. THEY SPECIFY THAT THE MURDERER WILL BE A LONER—TALL, UNDERNOURISHED, PHYSICALLY UNCLEAN—AND HE WILL CONTINUE TO KILL UNLESS CAUGHT. THIS TURNS OUT TO BE ACCURATE IN EVERY DETAIL.

ON JANUARY 27, 1978, THE KILLER COMMITS HIS FINAL MURDER, WHICH ALSO QUALIFIES THE CRIME AS A MASS MURDER. AWARE OF THE FBI PROFILE, A YOUNG WOMAN, NANCY HOLDEN, TELLS POLICE SHE BELIEVES RICHARD CHASE COULD BE THE KILLER. DETECTIVES FOLLOW THIS UP AND DISCOVER CHASE POSSESSES A .22-CALIBER SEMIAUTOMATIC PISTOL. AS HE LEAVES HIS APARTMENT THEY POUNCE. HIS COAT AND SHOES ARE BLOODSTAINED, AS IS A BOX HE IS CARRYING. INSIDE THE APARTMENT IS THE BLOODSTAINED .22 WITH WHICH HIS VICTIMS HAVE BEEN DISPATCHED.

Before the end of World War II, Dr. Walter C. Langer is asked by the Office of Strategic Services (OSS) to create a profile of Adolf Hitler. They want to find out about his possible behavioral patterns and what his reaction is likely to be if Germany loses the war. Dr. Langer's profile finds Hitler to be fastidious, orthodox, modest about his body and appearance, and slightly in love with his mother. He is afraid of germs, syphilis, and moonlight. He is fascinated by severed heads, urine and excrement, and shows distinctive signs of sadism. He is delusional and incapable of forging close relationships.

Dr. Langer is convinced that if the war is lost Hitler will probably commit suicide. Two years later this is exactly what happens.

BAD TO THE BONE

Is the psychopathic criminal somehow different from the rest of us from the day he enters the world?

By the time he was nine the German monster dubbed the "Düsseldorf sadist," Peter Kurten, had drowned two friends. Carl Panzram, the serial killer, wrote, "All of my family are as the average human beings are. They are honest and hard working people. All except myself. I have been a human-animile [sic] ever since I was born. When I was very young at five or six years of age I was a thief and a lier [sic] and a mean despicable one at that. The older I got the meaner I got."

TETEN, MULLANY, AND RESSLER—HUNTING A KILLER

In 1972 the FBI's Behavioral Science Unit is created in Quantico, Virginia, and Howard Teten, Patrick Mullany, and Robert Ressler are part of the team. They put to use their offender profiling technique to find the killer of a seven-year-old girl in Montana. Their profile notes that the abductor is probably a young white male—a "peeping Tom"—who retains body parts of his victims as souvenirs.

This leads to the apprehension of twenty-three-year-old David Meirhofer, already suspected in another murder case. The subsequent search of his property does indeed result in the grisly recovery of souvenirs from both victims. Meirhofer is the first sexual killer to be tracked down using this new FBI technique.

MOTIVE

Early record examination into crime detection depends largely on finding a link between victim and killer and establishing a motive for the crime. This is certainly the case with Gilles de Rais, a fifteenth-century French nobleman, who fights alongside Joan of Arc at Orleans. Secretly he is also molesting and killing hundreds of children. The homicidal pedophile is also a satanist and alchemist who uses the children's blood in a fanciful effort to turn lead into gold. Once identified for what he truly is and convicted, de Rais is strangled to death and then burned by the church for his heinous crimes.

MURDEROUS CHILDREN

The following are some characteristics purported to be exhibited by the child who has the capacity to kill:

- The absence of empathy
- A mother who was abused or deprived as a child
- When touched, an inability to make eye contact
- Cruelty toward other children
- Cruelty toward animals
- A disappearing father
- Easily frustrated
- No remorse for hurting another
- Poor relationships with adults
- Narcissistic
- Complications at birth or low birth weight
- A mother who finds it difficult to emotionally interact with the child

THE PSYCHOPATH

"They don't have the internal psychologist structure to feel and relate to other people...Sometimes they can imitate it, so they can fool other people, but there will come a point when they can't maintain it. It gives the psychopath the ability at times to kill without remorse and to kill for reasons filled with banality. Others' emotions of grief and rage and fury are like water off a duck's back."

Reid Maloy—forensic psychologist

A KILLER'S SIGNATURE

John Douglas, legendary profiler at the FBI Academy in Quantico, Virginia, has worked on many high-profile serial murder cases, including the "Atlanta Child Murders" and the "Green River Killer" cases. He is also part of a team of FBI agents sent to interview some fifty incarcerated serial killers in an attempt to understand and learn from their sociopathic behavioral patterns.

Douglas insists that the killer's signature is more revealing than his M.O. As the killer improves his "technique" his M.O. may alter but the emotional reason for his crimes is constant: "a personal detail that is unique to the individual; why he does it: the thing that fulfills him emotionally."

ANALYSIS AND ADVICE

FORENSIC PSYCHOLOGISTS ARE ACKNOWLEDGED FOR THEIR INVOLVEMENT IN THE CRIMINAL LEGAL SYSTEM. THEY PROVIDE COURTS WITH ANALYSIS PERTINENT TO QUESTIONS OF CRIMINAL INSANITY AND TRIAL COMPETENCE, AND ADVISE COURTS AS TO DECISIONS OVER WHETHER SEX OFFENDERS ARE LIKELY TO REOFFEND AND REMAIN A DANGER. FORENSIC PSYCHOLOGISTS ARE OFTEN CALLED UPON IN CAPITAL MURDER—OR DEATH PENALTY—CASES AND WILL OFFER ANALYSIS OF THE MOTIVATIONS AND PERSONALITY CHARACTERISTICS OF THE ACCUSED.

COMPETENCY TO STAND TRIAL (CST)

Does the defendant have the mental capacity to understand and/or appreciate the charges against him and assist his attorney in his defense? This is stated in the Sixth Amendment to the U.S. Constitution, which ensures the right to attend your trial, face your accusers, and be supported by an attorney. "Fitness to plead" is its British—English, Scottish, Northern Irish, and Welsh—counterpart.

A QUESTION OF MENTAL ILLNESS

A forensic psychiatrist can give an opinion as to whether a defendant was capable of understanding what he was doing at the time the crime was being committed. This is worded differently in many U.S. states, rejected out of hand in some. What is universal, however, is the intent to commit a criminal act and the ability to appreciate that it was a criminal act. This determines the final disposition in a case.

INSANITY

Forensic psychiatry is guided largely by significant court rulings or laws. Insanity is a legal, not a medical, term, when deciding if a person must stand trial or not, or whether he belongs in the prison system or an institution. Psychiatrists can appear on behalf of their defense or the prosecution.

EVALUATING ILLNESS

Forensic psychiatrists are responsible for evaluating prisoners and mentally ill hospital patients.

Albert von Schrenk-Notzing testifies at the trial of a man accused of killing three women. This is in 1896 and it is among the first examples of a psychologist being an expert witness in a court of law. Referring to his research into memory and suggestibility he maintains that witnesses cannot differentiate between what they have actually seen and what, thanks to pretrial publicity, has been reported in the newspapers.

THE PSYCHIATRIST AND THE SERIAL KILLER

At his 1983 trial, Dennis Andrew Nilsen is charged with six counts of murder and two charges of attempted murder. He pleads "Not Guilty" to all, claiming diminished responsibility. The defense relies on testimony from psychiatrists.

Dr. Patrick Gallwey diagnoses Nilsen as suffering from a "False Self Syndrome," which is manifested by outbreaks of schizoid disturbances. The jury are confused by his complex technical jargon.

Dr. Paul Bowden finds that Nilsen suffers from no such mental abnormalities. The jury decide to accept Bowden's testimony and Nilsen is convicted. He is sentenced to life imprisonment, without eligibility for parole for at least twenty-five years.

ALBERT DESALVO: HYPNOTIZING THE BOSTON STRANGLER

In 1964 the controversial decision is made to hypnotize Albert DeSalvo, aka "The Boston Strangler." Dr. William Bryan conducts the hypnosis, which involves putting DeSalvo into a trance. To demonstrate its effectiveness he jabs a needle into DeSalvo's arm and the alleged multiple killer does not flinch.

DeSalvo is then regressed in time to the date of one of the murders he is said to have committed. He describes the event in vivid detail. Bryan is accused of continual leading of the witness but detectives working the case are impressed. Forensic hypnosis, a rarity in the sixties, is still used today and this technique is more commonly employed to determine the accuracy of eyewitness testimony at trial.

THE LIE MACHINE

In 1921, John Larson invents the modern lie detector, known as the polygraph, at the University of California. The polygraph will remain controversial and is not always legally acceptable. In using the device sensors are attached to different parts of the body and the polygraph monitors any changes in pulse, blood pressure, breathing, or perspiration by recording the information on graph paper. These changes are apparently brought about by involuntary physiological reactions caused by stress when a person tells a lie.

SHE SAW TED

Nita Neary returns to the Chi Omega sorority house, Tallahassee, Florida, in January, 1978, to find a man running down the stairs. She ducks out of view but glimpses his profile. She proceeds to learn that the sinister figure has viciously attacked four other girls in the house, two of whom are already dead. Nita is put into a hypnotic state and then questioned. From a police photo lineup she selects a photograph of Ted Bundy.

Approximately one month later, twelve-year-old Kimberly Diane Leach is abducted and brutally murdered. Clarence Anderson is the only witness to the abduction. He undergoes hypnosis twice to refresh his memory. He too identifies Ted Bundy.

THE POLYGRAPH: GETTING TO THE TRUTH OF THE MATTER

The use of a polygraph to indicate deception is the most controversial of all the forensic disciplines. The lie detector has been around for over seventy years and has been the cause of dissension for most of that time. The most common polygraph technique, the comparative question, is at the center of the argument. Detractors have accused this technique, formerly known as the control question technique, of lacking validity and of being incomplete because of its still experimental nature. Others admit that further research is required but hold that the quality of the accessible field data indicates an accuracy of approximately ninety percent.

THE HILLSIDE ACTOR

One of the Hillside Stranglers, Kenneth Bianchi, develops an ingenious scheme to escape the death penalty for his role in the killings. A fan of the film Sybil, about a girl who is a schizophrenic suffering from multiple personalities, Bianchi reprises her role while "hypnotized." During sessions with Dr. John Watkins, Bianchi introduces him to an evil psychopath called Steve Walker, who allegedly dwells within him and takes great pride in confessing to the killings.

Bianchi is so convincing that he dupes both Dr. Watkins and another expert in the field, Dr. Ralph Allison. However L.A. detective Frank Salerno, who has been watching the performance, is far from convinced and, along with Dr. Martin Orne, sets a trap for Bianchi.

Orne "accidentally" lets slip that multiple personality disorder usually involves more than one alternative personality and predictably, during Bianchi's next session, "Billy" appears, followed by yet another two trapped souls. Orne's testimony shatters the defense and Bianchi soon accepts a plea bargain as a means of escaping the gas chamber.

CHEATING THE MACHINE?

At times an individual's responses to the polygraph test are unclear. Results could be affected by drug or alcohol usage; even being hungry could be a taken as a relevant consideration when testing.

For those intent on deception, and presumably versed in how to cheat the "lie-box," inducing pain by, for example, biting on a cheek or tongue is thought to affect the results. And often the apprehension and anxiety caused by facing the test not only makes responses unclear but can actually result in a suspect changing their plea from innocent to guilty out of fright.

SWEET AND SOUR CHINESE

In ancient China it is said the following impressive technique was used:

When a man was being interrogated he had a small portion of dry rice put under his tongue and was ordered to keep it there. After questioning he had to spit the rice out into his hand. The happy man whose rice was wet with saliva was not beheaded. The unfortunate man whose rice was still dry lost his head. This illustrates a well known philosophy—a person's mouth goes dry under stressful circumstances! With the exception of the hardened psychopath, stress will often lead to a guilty person's undoing.

Paperwork and Tax Returns

"For many forgers the ultimate goal is not to get rich by swindling easy marks but to see their fabrications touted as authentic by historians."

Charles Hamilton (from his book *Great Forgers and Famous Fakes*)

FORENSIC ACCOUNTING

Forensic accounting is the analysis of documents like bank statements and tax returns to unearth criminal activities, whether this is a case of fraud or tax evasion. Organized crime is all about making money illegally; a definite paper trail is created as cash comes into and then out of the organization.

This is the method used to convict Chicago mob boss Al Capone of tax evasion in 1931. Following business scandals like Enron, forensic accounting has become better known but it actually goes back a long way. A court decision involving a bankrupt estate in 1817 was thanks to an early type of forensic accounting.

FAMILY BUSINESS

Forensic accountants spend two years scrutinizing financial documents, finally unearthing the proof of the criminal pursuits of Bonanno crime family boss Joseph Massino and his associates. If not for the evidence exposed by these investigators, federal prosecutors would never have got their hands on Massino for the murders of Dominick "Big Trin" Trinchera, Philip "Philly Lucky" Giaccone and Alphonse "Sonny Red" Indelicato (dramatized in the movie *Donnie Brasco*, based on the story of undercover FBI agent Joseph D. Pistone who successfully infiltrated the Bonannos for a six-year period), along with a handful of others.

NOT AN EASY TASK FOR THE FORGER

No two people have identical handwriting. For this reason it is not easy to forge or disguise. Handwriting analysis, then, is an important method of incriminating a suspect. This subdivision of forensic science involves the comparison and authentication of written documents such as forged wills, fake passports and I.D.s, ransom notes, and any other type of printed or written work. The shape, slant, and size of single letters are examined and noted along with similarities between vocabulary, spelling, grammar, and punctuation. A comparison is usually made between a sample from a suspect and an unidentified document.

THE HITLER DIARIES

In 1981, a great historical find is discovered. Twenty-seven volumes of Adolf Hitler's diaries and an unpublished third volume of Mein Kampf in Hitler's own handwriting are bought by a German publisher for $2.3 million. Despite experts testifying to the authenticity of the diaries, tests reveal otherwise. Testing the paper under ultraviolet light, a whitening agent is discovered that was made in 1954, nine years after Hitler's death. Also the seals contain viscose and polyester, developed well after the end of WWII. Finally the chloride evaporation from the ink is tested and reveals the ink had been on the paper for less than a year. Konrad Kujau, a German forger, admits to producing the "diaries."

QUESTIONED DOCUMENTS

The questioned document examiner concentrates on the identification of handwriting, alterations, indentations, obliterations, and different types of ink. A document is anything that carries a message that can be written, reproduced, or copied. Handwriting identification is based on the supposition that no two people have identical handwriting.

The fact is that even an individual cannot exactly reproduce his own handwriting. Handwriting identification is determined by a full and comparative analysis between the handwriting of the suspect and that of the questioned document. Particular characteristics and singular traits of both the samples and the questioned document are studied for differences and similarities.

HAROLD SHIPMAN'S FAMOUS LAST WORDS

Dr. Harold Shipman has killed many of his patients for profit and pleasure without detection for many years. Shipman murders Mrs. Kathleen Grundy and forges a new will, as he has done many times before, leaving £386,000 (about US$745,000) to him. However, Mrs. Grundy's daughter, Mrs. Angela Woodruff, is a lawyer, and her mother made a will at her own practice in 1986. She has no knowledge of this new will, the phraseology is nothing like the previous will, and she is deeply suspicious.

The police share her suspicions and Mrs. Grundy's body is exhumed for examination; a detailed investigation into Shipman follows. His typewriter is discovered and the type matches the fake will exactly. Shipman knows the net is closing in and bizarrely claims to have lent his typewriter to Mrs. Grundy. He also falsifies appointments, suggesting that Mrs. Grundy was addicted to morphine, the drug used to murder her.

What Shipman fails to realize is that these records can be easily checked for alterations, and police find that they were changed after her death. He is subsequently arrested.

YOU CAN TELL BY THE SIGNATURE

A common mistake made by amateur forgers is that a person's signature is always identical. That could not be further from the truth, however. Although it will always have similar characteristics, such as the sloping or shape of letters, each signature will usually be different. Whether the signature was written formally or casually, differing types of pen, and natural aging, can all affect a person's signature. If a suspect signature is placed over a genuine signature on a light box, and the two match exactly, investigators will automatically suspect forgery.

THAT'S NOTHING LIKE MY WRITING!

Not all forged documents are made to resemble someone else's handwriting. In some cases (such as ransom notes) criminals will try to disguise their own handwriting. Changing the direction of the slant in writing, writing in block capitals, deliberate misspellings, and writing with the wrong hand, are all tricks of the trade. However, most experts discount these obvious methods and focus instead on individual letters. For example, the way people write individual letters or how the writer begins or ends a letter every time it appears, is far harder to disguise. Also a suspect's home or office may be searched for previous drafts of the documents, or an imprint of the document left on pages of a notebook or blotter pad.

ART FORGERY

The canvas used for an oil painting is not a reliable indication of age. The weave composition could give some clue but a forger could have obtained and cleaned off an old canvas from another artist. The frame is the most accurate means of dating, as the study of tree ring measurements can provide the age of the wood. Art forgers, despite often thinking themselves too "talented" and feeling decidedly invulnerable because they perceive this to be a "victimless" crime, can face prison time if convicted.

LIGHTING

Infrared light can disclose whether paint or ink was used in the painting and ultraviolet light becomes fluorescent blue-green if the varnish is nineteenth century. If these measures are unhelpful, forensic scientists can take a small sample of paint from a damaged area or the edge of the painting and subsequently deposit it in cold-setting polymer. Once under a microscope its pigment can be identified.

BENEATH THE MICROSCOPE

Probably the easiest means of examining a painting is in the laboratory. Forensic scientists can tell the age of a painting by using a microscope. Forgers reproduce old, cracked surfaces by rolling the canvas, then heating and cooling it in quick succession. Finally they apply a constricting varnish with a stippling brush. However X-rays show whether the cracks appear on every layer of the painting or under the surface. With most forgeries a cracked appearance is only on the top layer and does not correspond to the bottom layer.

CAUGHT OUT WITH NEWTON

POSSIBLY THE MOST WONDERFULLY RIDICULOUS HOAX IN THE WORLD OF FORGERY WAS COMMITTED BY DENIS VRAIN-LUCAS. IN 1861 HE SELLS A COLLECTION OF FORGERIES WHICH COMPRISE 27,000 DOCUMENTS, TO A FAMOUS FRENCH MATHEMATICIAN. THESE ARE NOT SKILFULLY EXECUTED—ALL ARE WRITTEN IN MODERN FRENCH. VRAIN-LUCAS IS RISKING ALL ON THE GULLIBILITY OF THE BUYER.

THE DOCUMENTS INCLUDE LETTERS BY ALEXANDER THE GREAT, ATTILA THE HUN, JOAN OF ARC, MARY MAGDALENE, PONTIUS PILATE, LAZARUS (EITHER SIDE OF HIS RESURRECTION!), JUDAS ISCARIOT AND LOVE LETTERS BETWEEN CAESAR AND CLEOPATRA. VRAIN-LUCAS COMES TO GRIEF HOWEVER WHEN HE ATTEMPTS TO CONVINCE ROBERT BOYLE (VIA A FORGED LETTER), THAT BLAISE PASCAL AND NOT NEWTON DISCOVERED THE LAWS OF GRAVITY. IF THE DATE ON THE FORGED LETTER IS TO BE BELIEVED, IT WOULD HAVE MADE NEWTON, AT THE TIME OF WRITING, ONLY TEN YEARS OLD.

Hughes Identifies a Phoney

Clifford Irving is one of history's most insolent forgers. Irving forges an "autobiography" of Howard Hughes whilst its subject is still alive and sells it for a huge amount of money ($750,000) to a publisher—McGraw-Hill. To help sell his book he produces forged handwritten letters of Hughes. When the authenticity of the work is questioned, McGraw-Hill employ a handwriting expert who declares the manuscript genuine. But then Howard Hughes decides, after fourteen years, to speak to a reporter. He says, "The book is a phoney and Clifford is a phoney."

PRAISE TO THE MASTER

Many painters during the Renaissance employ apprentices who copy the style of their masters during the study of painting techniques. The master will usually sell these paintings in payment for their training. This concept is not considered forgery but as praise to the master. Back even further in time Roman sculptors sold copies of Greek sculptures. During this period art was used for religious inspiration and historical reference. In recent times Charles Hamilton in his book *Great Forgers and Famous Fakes* says, "For many forgers the ultimate goal is not to get rich by swindling easy marks but to see their fabrications touted as authentic by historians."

ART FORGERY—SOME METHODS OF AUTHENTICATION

- Carbon dating—measures age up to 10,000 years old.

- White lead —measures age up to 1,600 years old.

- Infrared and ultraviolet uncover any repairs to the canvass.

- X-ray—used to indicate if there is an earlier painting underneath the present one.

- Fluorescence reveals whether materials used are more recent than their given age or too pure.

- Diffraction indicates the composition of the paint.

- Thermoluminescence (TL) dates pottery.

- Stable isotope—used in sculpture, shows where the marble was quarried.

- Dendrochronolgy—used in wood, counts the number of tree rings in the object.

ANCIENT FORGERIES

The monetary value of objects declared to be thousands of years old is very great. Archaeological forgeries almost always ensue from the discovery of important archaeological excavations. Notable digs such as those at Pompeii, Crete, and of course The Valley of the Kings in Egypt are responsible for the arrival on the scene of forgeries claimed to have been stolen from the sites. Most of these are sold quite openly but others have been the subject of genuine historical study and have even found their way into museum collections.

An Artist's Impression

"Just a demonstrative aid."

State v. Dunkle, 2003

COMPOSITE DRAWINGS

Composite drawings, probably the most familiar service of forensic artists, are powerful aids to police investigations. Composites are primarily drawn to identify suspects of crime or indeed eliminate suspects—in this way valuable time and expense is saved in interrogation, checking out alibis, etc. Composites are a fast method of distribution to the media, ensuring public involvement.

IDENTIKIT

The Identikit is first developed in the 1950s in an era when composite imagery development from multiple witnesses is the norm. It is a tool that helps in the capture of mass murderers such as notorious slayer of eight Chicago nurses Richard Speck and serial killers like Harvey Glatman, the jug-eared rapist and murderer of two models. Another other young woman, who is coincidentally arrested by Detective Pierce Brooks, whose later brainchild is the hugely successful VICAP (Violent Criminal Apprehension Program) now overseen by the FBI at Quantico, Virginia.

IDENTIKIT 2000

Identikit 2000 is still a composite approach to identification of suspects, but a computerized version. Witnesses see a whole face within the range of their description and not individual facial parts. The artist then alters the incorrect features using the comprehensive database. The composite can then be sent via computer to other agencies.

AN EXPERT WITNESS

In major murder trials the "expert witness" is normally a scientific expert specializing in a particular field, like drug analysis, blood splatter patterns, DNA comparison, etc. They may simply be called upon to offer expertise but sometimes they are involved in the investigation itself.

The following criteria for qualification as an expert witness have been indicated in a recent article:

Undergraduate and graduate degrees in the relevant field of expertise;

Some training in forensics;

Specialized training in the subject area as it relates to forensic science;

Evidence for experimentation, teaching, and publication within the specialty area;

Professional licenses or certifications required by professional groups in the expert's discipline;

Prior disciplinary evidence directly relevant to the issues being considered.

FALSELY IDENTIFIED?

ON THE NIGHT OF AUGUST 22, 1961, MICHAEL GREGSTEN AND HIS MISTRESS VALERIE STORIE ARE FORCED TO DRIVE AWAY WITH A GUN-TOTING ASSAILANT WHO HAS JUST ENTERED THEIR CAR. MR. GREGSTEN IS SOON SHOT DEAD; MISS STORIE IS RAPED, AND THEN SHOT. THE ATTACKER, THINKING HER DEAD TOO, FLEES THE SCENE.

WHEN POLICE EVENTUALLY HAUL IN JAMES HANRATTY, BASED ON THE FACT THAT THEY HAVE RECOVERED TWO BULLET CARTRIDGE CASES FROM HIS HOTEL ROOM THAT BELONG TO THE MURDER WEAPON, THEY ARE CERTAIN THEY HAVE THEIR MAN. IN ADDITION, TWO IDENTIKITS OF THE KILLER, BASED ON DESCRIPTIONS GIVEN BY THE SURVIVING VICTIM AND NOTABLE FOR THE SUSPECT'S DEEP-SET BROWN EYES, ARE COMPARED WITH HIM.

HANRATTY DOES NOT LOOK MUCH LIKE EITHER. DESPITE THIS HE IS FOUND GUILTY AND HANGED. DOUBT OVER HIS CONVICTION HAS PERSISTED FOR DECADES AND THERE ARE MANY WHO BELIEVE THE REAL KILLER GOT AWAY.

THE CECIL COURT ANTIQUE SHOP MURDER

On Friday March 3, 1961, in London, England, fifty-nine-year-old Elsie Batten is found stabbed to death in her Cecil Court antique shop. Detective Sergeant Raymond Dagg of Bow Street uses a new American concept—the Identikit. A facial picture of the suspect is compiled and appears in newspapers. Edwin Bush is later arrested and has a newspaper clipping of the Identikit picture in his pocket. The soles of his shoes are found to be consistent with marks left at the crime scene and a paper-wrapped dress sword, stolen from Mrs. Batten's shop, bears Bush's palm print. He is convicted and executed at Pentonville Prison in 1961.

IMAGE ENHANCEMENT

Using the science of image enhancement, an artist is able to add features such as eyeglasses, moustaches, beards, hair styles, and numerous other items to an impression of a suspect as applicable. This process is extremely useful for aiding in the location of armed robbery suspects and modernizing outdated photographs of wanted criminals and fugitives of justice.

AGE PROGRESSION

Family members of a loved one who has been missing for an extended period of time, along with investigators, can be aided by computer-generated and hand-drawn age progressions. These can be used in the identification of a suspect as well as that of a missing person. Age progression is most commonly used to assist in apprehension of wanted fugitives, where the only available pictures are outdated.

WHERE'S WHITEY?

AN EXAMPLE OF IMAGE ENHANCEMENT USED IN 2000 IN THE HUNT FOR AN EXCEPTIONALLY DANGEROUS FUGITIVE IS THAT OF REPUTED BOSTON MOB OVERLORD JAMES "WHITEY" BULGER, WHO SUCCESSFULLY FLED HIS FBI PURSUERS AND WAS PLACED HIGH IN THE RANKINGS OF AMERICA'S "MOST WANTED" BULLETIN BOARD AND WEBSITE. THROUGH A COMPUTER-GENERATED PROCESS OF AGE PROGRESSION, USING IMAGES OF HOW BULGER MAY NOW LOOK, THE FEDERAL GOVERNMENT HOPE TO ALERT TO THE POSSIBLE PRESENCE OF THIS PROLIFIC AND NOTORIOUS MULTIPLE MURDERER—BUT CERTAINLY DO NOT UNDER ANY CIRCUMSTANCES ADVOCATE AN APPROACH.

The use of fingerprints to link suspects to the crime scene goes back to the nineteenth century, but this process is only possible if you can actually see the fingerprint. The killer leaves a clue behind—a bloody fingerprint on the bedsheet.

Naturally investigators will use the best known technique of identification, mapping the whorls and loops of skin ridges found at the scene and comparing them with the fingerprints of the suspect. But wait—there is a problem. It is impossible to see the fingerprint properly because of the vivid pattern on the sheet.

It is NASA who comes to the rescue of detectives from Los Angeles County Sheriff's Department. They are able to subtract the background pattern, thus leaving only the fingerprint, by using imaging techniques put into practice whilst enhancing photographs of distant planets.

FACIAL RECONSTRUCTION

Forensic facial reconstruction is the science of recreating the face of an unidentified person using their skeletal remains. The process involves a combination of anthropology, osteology, forensic science, anatomy, and, of course, artistic imagery. Because of the latter it is a controversial technique, as it is necessarily subjective. It has, however, been successful enough to warrant continued development and research and is acknowledged as a most important tool in crime detection.

THE FACIAL RECONSTRUCTION OF JANE DOE

In March, 1998, Viki Hartigan begins a facial reconstruction for the Lyon County Sheriffs. The forensic anthropologist's report indicates the victim is a female in her twenties.

Reconstruction is made difficult owing to the skull missing the maxilla above the front teeth, the mandible, and almost all teeth, with just four remaining.

Hartigan consults a chart used to determine measurements of tissue thickness at certain landmarks on the skull. She uses modelling clay and an artistic technique to complete the reconstruction.

Vickie explains: "I would consult the chart for female Caucasian in the age range they gave me and mark the landmarks on the skull with erasers. Because they indicated to me that they thought she might be a transient, I didn't know if her identity would ever be found out or not. If you can find a picture or if you can find a family member or somebody that knew the person, you'll almost always have identification because everyone's skull is unique."

SUPERIMPOSITION

A method of forensic facial reconstruction sometimes employed is the technique of "superimposition." This is produced by superimposing a photograph of a person thought to have been the unidentified skeletal remains onto an X-ray of the unidentified skull. The anatomical features of the face should be uniform if the photograph and the skull are of the same person.

THE PICTURE IN THE PAPER

In February 2003, U.S. investigators discover the unidentified body of a black male in a Miami medical supply warehouse. The victim has been shot and his remains are badly decomposed. A facial reconstruction is performed over the course of two days. Frontal and profile views of the slain man are created. An amazing likeness to the victim is the result.

The sketch is released to the media in April. After seeing the drawings in the newspaper, the victim's parents come forward to inform investigators that the image depicts their son, Tyshon.

Twenty-eight-year-old Tyshon Brown is positively identified when his fingerprints from a prior arrest are compared to partial prints lifted from the corpse.

TRACKING JOHN LIST

In 1971 John Emil List shoots dead his mother, wife, and three children, then disappears. Nearly twenty years later forensic artists bring about his downfall.

In 1988, using List's photograph, the FBI employ computerized photographic enhancement in an attempt to discover what he would now look like. Later that year, forensic sculptor Frank Bender makes a three-dimensional clay bust using his expertise to portray the passage of time on facial features. Amazingly somebody recognizes the wanted fugitive. Although List protests his innocence, fingerprint evidence confirms his identity, leading to his conviction for five counts of murder.

SUBJECTIVITY

Because of the subjectivity of artistic imagery, the reconstruction shows only what the face of the individual may have looked like in life. Broadly speaking, the shape and position of the main facial features, determined by the skull, will be fairly precise. However, because the skeletal remains leave no trace of their appearance, distinctions such as the shape of the ears and nose, facial wrinkles and birthmarks, can only be guessed at.

REALITY AND IMAGINATION

THE AIM OF FORENSIC FACIAL RECONSTRUCTION IS TO TAKE A SKULL AND CREATE AN ADEQUATE LIKENESS OF THAT PERSON WHEN ALIVE. THIS WILL THEN AID IN THE IDENTIFICATION OF THE REMAINS WHEN THERE IS NOTHING ELSE TO HELP. THE NINETEENTH CENTURY SEES THE FIRST ATTEMPTS AT FACIAL RECONSTRUCTION BUT THE PROCESS BECOMES INFAMOUS IN 1968 WHEN USED BY GERASIMOV IN THE FILM "GORKY PARK." ORTHODOX METHODS USE PLASTICINE OR MODELLING CLAY TO BUILD UP THE DEPTH OF TISSUE ON THE SKULL TO RESEMBLE A LIVING PERSON. IT IS, HOWEVER, IMPOSSIBLE TO PREDICT THE SHAPE OF THE MOUTH, NOSE AND EYES, AND HERE THE PRACTITIONER WILL USE HIS IMAGINATION. THIS MEANS THE RESULTS WILL VARY BETWEEN DIFFERENT PRACTITIONERS AND THEIR RECONSTRUCTIONS.

INADEQUATE DATA CONCERNING TISSUE THICKNESS

The information supplied to forensic artists is limited in the areas of sex, age and body build. This deficiency affects the accuracy of the reconstructions a great deal. Inadequate data make things difficult for the artist and it is often requested that supporting evidence, if applicable, be presented so as to combine other clues which may help them in their quest.

LACK OF STANDARDIZATION
A standard, official technique for reconstructing the face does not exist. This is a major hitch to reconstruction, particularly with individual features like hairstyles and facial characteristics like the nose and eyes, i.e., the features probably most easily remembered by a witness.

FORENSIC ANIMATION

The employment of "animation" in the courtroom has increased dramatically over the last few years. Animation provides powerful visual displays ensuring the attention of the jurors throughout a trial and deliberation. They are able to perceive and indeed believe the evidence of one lawyer over another by means of these images. Animations are being substituted for more traditional display methods such as graphs, charts, PowerPoint and videos because they can so forcefully demonstrate a story.

THE COMPUTER-GENERATED CRIME SCENE

While extremely helpful in most cases, sometimes an animation can prove misleading. Laura Dunkle, the girlfriend of Gary Benton White, is charged with his murder after he is shot outside their home. At her trial, evidence is introduced by way of a computer-generated crime scene created with the help of a crime scene reconstruction expert. Dunkle's lawyers oppose the admissibility of the animation but this is rejected as the reenactment is declared "just a demonstrative aid," and Dunkle is found guilty. She appeals, citing the animations as a key issue.

TELEFORENSICS

TELEFORENSICS IS A BURGEONING NEW TECHNOLOGY THAT CAN ENABLE AN INVESTIGATOR TO BE AT THE CRIME SCENE EVEN IF HE IS ON THE OTHER SIDE OF THE WORLD. AN IMAGE OF A CRIME SCENE IS CAPTURED ON IMAGE AND SENT TO AN EXPERT TO HELP WITH ANALYSIS. IT WORKS BY DIGITIZING INFORMATION AND BOUNCING IT OFF SATELLITES OR SENDING IT DOWN TELEPHONE LINES SO THAT ONE OR SEVERAL EXPERTS CAN LOOK AT IT AND DISCUSS IT WITH ONE ANOTHER. MUCH MORE FUNDING IS REQUIRED IN ORDER TO DEVELOP THIS TECHNOLOGY.

CONTAMINATION

A detective at the crime scene sneezes and thousands of microscopic droplets of bacteria hurtle towards potential evidence. He uses gloves to pick up a piece of evidence, speaks to a colleague, and saliva contaminates that evidence. Unaware that invaluable trace evidence adheres to his shoes, he leaves behind shoe prints. But the time has arrived when we need no longer be anxious about carrying away trace evidence or contaminating the area with DNA. Thanks to the advent of teleforensics, apart from a few personnel physically gathering evidence at the scene, investigators and forensic scientists will view the area from a remote location, sharing crime scene information without the risk of contamination.

EXAMINING MUMMIES

The usual method of examining mummies until relatively recently was first to carefully unwrap them and then to perform an autopsy. However, not only did this mar the original appearance of the mummy, it also ruined all records of the wrapping. In 1898 X-rays are introduced into the process in order to permit study without unwrapping but these can only show the images of bone and not soft tissue. Then in the 1960s CT scans are tested and deemed fit to be used for this reconstructive method. These create images of fat and muscle in addition to bone. Contiguous images are stacked together to create three-dimensional reconstructions.

AN ART FORM

THE "UMBRELLA" TERM "FORENSIC ART" ENCOMPASSES ANY ART THAT FACILITATES, FOR EXAMPLE, THE IDENTIFICATION OF CRIMINALS, OR ANONYMOUS DECEASED INDIVIDUALS. ANOTHER TASK MAY BE TO ASSIST IN FINDING MISSING CHILDREN (AGE PROGRESSION). THE ARTISTS INVOLVED IN THIS PARTICULAR FIELD NEED TO LEARN THE COMPLICATED PATTERNS OF CRANIOFACIAL GROWTH IN ORDER TO PRODUCE AGE PROGRESSIONS TO CREATE THE FACES OF CHILDREN WHO HAVE BEEN MISSING A LONG TIME. SOMETIMES THE TASK IS TO FIND FUGITIVES (UPDATES). IN THIS CASE THE ARTIST WILL NEED TO BE AN EXPERT IN ANATOMY IN ORDER TO ACCURATELY PREDICT BIOLOGICAL AGING. OTHER TYPES OF INVESTIGATIVE ARTWORK INVOLVE IDENTIFYING BODIES, EITHER THROUGH FACIAL RECONSTRUCTION OR POSTMORTEM SKETCHES.

RECONSTRUCTING MAGNUSSON'S FACE

At a time in early Swedish history the "Prime Minister" of the day was Birger Magnusson (1210-1266). It is during his administration that the origins of an organized Swedish nation are established. Because no pictures of his face survive, the purpose of the reconstruction is to give historians and researchers an impression of what the great man looked like. His body is exhumed in 2002 and in place of the usual CT scanning a new technique, that of a videosequence of the skull, is provided to enable artists to create a 3-D reconstruction of the face of Sweden's first Prime Minister.

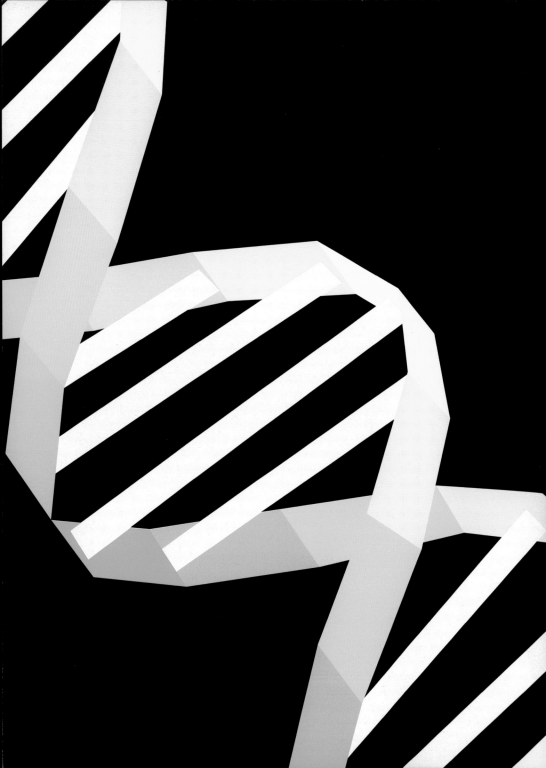

Precious Fluids

"Advances in modern science techniques should stand as a warning that there is no hiding place for sexual and violent criminals."

Judge Gerald Gordon, Old Bailey, 2001

HENRY LEE ASSISTS

Serology is the analysis of serums, i.e., blood, saliva, semen, sweat, and feces, and forensic expert Henry C. Lee knows them well. He has assisted in thousands of investigations, perhaps most notably the double slayings for which O.J. Simpson would go on trial in 1995. Lee attests that blood is found mostly in "crimes of violence such as homicide, assault, and sexual assault." Serological evidence will be found variously as fresh, dry, coagulated, and in droplets or stains. In criminal cases blood establishes blood pattern analysis (BPA) as well as group and gender.

BLOOD PATTERNING

WHEN A HOMICIDE HAS BEEN COMMITTED, THERE WILL OFTEN BE A PRESENCE OF BLOOD, WITH THE MORE VIOLENT CRIME LOGICALLY CREATING THE LARGER QUANTITY. A FORENSIC SCIENTIST WITH BLOODSTAINING AND PATTERNING EXPERIENCE WILL INVARIABLY BE CALLED TO THE SCENE TO DISTINGUISH BETWEEN WHAT JOHN GLAISTER, PROFESSOR OF FORENSIC MEDICINE AND PUBLIC HEALTH AT GLASGOW UNIVERSITY, SCOTLAND, DESCRIBES AS THE "SIX PATTERNS." THESE ARE: DROPS, SMEARS, TRAILS, POOLS, SPURTS, AND SPLASHES.

A DROP OF BLOOD

A drop of blood is caused by dripping and will be found on a horizontal surface such as the ground, a floor, table, etc. The size and shape of the droplet will vary according to the vertical distance it has traveled before making contact with a surface. The "starring" or crenellation of a drop will be more or less pronounced, depending on the height from which it has fallen.

BLOOD SMEARING

Typically, a wounded victim struggling for aid or escape will clutch at or cling to an object during their flight from an assailant. Equally, following an especially violent assault, an attacker covered in his victim's blood may also leave smearing if he comes into contact with objects such as furniture, doors, windows, and walls. A particular blood smear can speak volumes to an experienced investigator.

A TRAIL OF BLOOD

For various reasons, probably in the process of concealment or disposal, a homicide victim's body will sometimes be dragged across the ground for a distance by the attacker. This will leave a trail of blood in its wake. If the killer lifts or carries the corpse there will also more than likely be a trail of blood drops. This can tell an investigator much about a killer's thought processes in terms of his organizational skills or lack thereof at the crime scene.

BLOOD POOLING

Heavy, excessive bleeding from an injured or dying victim can result in a pool of blood. If a victim remains in one position for a period of time, bleeding copiously, the pool will begin to form. It goes without saying that the longer a victim remains sedentary the larger the pool of blood will become. In the case of a seriously wounded person navigating an area, pools of blood will be separated by smears and drops.

BLOOD SPURT

As blood is pumped by the heart through the body under a great pressure, a major artery or vein that is cut or opened will emit a forceful flow, referred to as a spurt. Due to this an assailant will probably be covered in blood, as will surrounding items at the crime location. If a victim is already dead when his or her body is cut, as in the case of dismemberment, this spurting will not be present. It is a valuable indicator as to whether a person was alive during certain stages of an attack.

BLOOD SPLASHES

When a series of blood droplets are propelled through the air, usually caused by a violent connective swing from a weapon designed to wreak maximum damage upon a victim, a stain commonly resembling an exclamation mark may later be found on a nearby surface. This often proves important in an investigation as it will help determine the actual location of the assault.

SECRETORS

AROUND EIGHTY PERCENT OF THE POPULATION QUALIFY AS "SECRETORS." THIS MEANS THAT PROTEINS, ENZYMES, ANTIGENS, AND ANTIBODIES THAT DISTINGUISH THEIR BLOOD ARE ALSO PRESENT IN OTHER BODILY SECRETIONS SUCH AS SEMEN, SWEAT, AND SALIVA.

SECRETORS ARE FAR MORE EASILY IDENTIFIED, AS THEIR SPECIFIC MAKEUP CAN BE LEFT BEHIND ALMOST ANYWHERE THEY GO. FOR EXAMPLE, THE SALIVA LEFT BEHIND ON THE BUTT OF A CIGARETTE CAN BE MATCHED EXACTLY AND PRECISELY AFTER A SMALL SWAB OF SALIVA IS TAKEN.

GEL ELECTROPHORESIS

Gel electrophoresis is a method of testing human blood by the movement of antibodies and antigens on a gel-coated plate which is subjected to an intense electrical field.

LIQUID CHROMATOGRAPHY

Liquid chromatography is a technique for separating complex mixtures into their constituents by dissolving the mixture in solution and passing it through a fine absorbent material.

THIN-LAYER CHROMATOGRAPHY

Thin-layer chromatography involves separating a liquid into its constituent parts by the speed in which they move by capillary action up a plate coated with a thin layer of silica gel.

THE DYNAMICS OF BLOOD

The average adult has around ten pints of blood coursing through their body driven by pressure from the heart. If a major artery or blood vessel is severed in an attack or accident, the blood will be pumped out of the body until the heart stops pumping it.

In cases where much blood has been spilled at a crime scene, it can become possible to approximately reconstruct a scenario of what happened from examining the spray, trail, or pools of blood left behind. If the attacker's blood is also shed at the scene, this can tie them to the crime as firmly as a photograph or eyewitness.

SEMINAL FLUID

In cases of rape and other sexually motivated crimes, the presence of seminal fluid left by the attacker on the victim's body, clothes, or furniture, is a key piece of evidence for forensic examiners. When the fluid belongs to a secretor, his blood group, along with the presence or absence of proteins or enzymes, can be found within the sample. It is also a valuable tool for building a DNA profile.

It also has other uses. Sperm within the fluid can only live for a very short time outside the body, so the condition of the sample can give a very good indication of the time of the attack. Traces of seminal fluid can be located using similar methods to bloodstains, and, as with blood, it is possible to demonstrate where the fluid has been—even if the attacker has tried to remove all trace of it ever having been there.

BLOOD AND BACTERIA

It is April 25, 1934. The victim is eight-year-old Helen Priestly. When Helen's body is discovered it appears as though she has been sexually assaulted as well as strangled. A subsequent postmortem examination, however, quickly establishes that the rape, or attempted rape, scenario has actually been manufactured. An instrument has been thrust into the child's body, perhaps in an effort to simulate intercourse.

A woman soon falls under suspicion. Her name is Jeannie Donald and she is faced with overwhelming evidence against her from chemists, biologists, and bacteriologists. Helen's underwear has bloodstains and bacteria traces. They match those found on articles in Mrs. Donald's flat. Jeannie Donald is convicted of Helen's murder and sentenced to death, later to be commuted to life imprisonment.

TESTING FOR BLOOD

A SIMPLE TEST FOR PEROXIDASE CAN BE APPLIED AT THE SCENE OF THE CRIME. IT MERELY DETERMINES WHETHER A SUBSTANCE CAN BE CLASSIFIED AS REAL BLOOD. PEROXIDASE IS ACTUALLY AN ENZYME FOUND IN BLOOD— IT TRIGGERS A REACTION FROM HYDROGEN PEROXIDE BY RELEASING OXYGEN. THERE ARE VARIATIONS ON THIS TYPE OF BASIC TEST, THE MOST COMMON BEING THE KASTLE-MEYER. JUST PLACE THE SUSPECT STAIN ON A PIECE OF FILTER PAPER; DROP PHENOLPHTHALEIN, ALCOHOL, AND HYDROGEN PEROXIDE ON TO THE EVIDENCE; AND A PINK REACTION WILL TAKE PLACE IF BLOOD IS DETECTED.

ASCERTAINING THE SOURCE OF BLOOD

Precipitin is a serum that is used to identify the proteins in the blood of any animal, including humans. In 1901 Paul Uhlenhuth (AN assistant professor at the University of Greifswald, Germany) injected protein from a chicken's egg into a rabbit. He combined the rabbit serum with egg white; this caused the egg proteins to separate from the clear liquid and form the cloudy precipitin. Today, this effect is achieved with electrodes to speed the process up; the results are just as conclusive. This test is indisputable.

THE MONSTER OF RüGEN

On a German island in 1901, these tests cut short Ludwig Tessnow's killing spree. The "Monster of Rügen," as he is dubbed, sexually assaults and murders two young children on the island, and then he scatters their dismembered limbs throughout the woodlands of the area.

Interestingly, just a few weeks earlier, he did the same to seven locally-owned sheep. In both cases he had been spotted in the area with dark stains on his clothes, which he attempted to explain away as wood dye. Fortunately, tests are done, and the stains are found to be blood, both human and sheep. Tessnow is convicted and of course executed for the heinous double child-murder.

BLOOD OF A SERIAL KILLER

On April 18, 2000, Robert L. Yates Jr. is arrested for the murder of Jennifer Joseph. During the autopsies of seven other murder victims, specimens have been gathered from their body cavities and orifices. These show the presence of human sperm, as specimens taken from the condom recovered from an eighth victim. DNA typing proves it belongs to the same perpetrator. At the time of Yates's arrest a search warrant is issued, allowing the authorities to collect blood samples from him. DNA analysis proves the match between the victims and Yates.

THE MURDER OF DR. SAM SHEPPARD'S WIFE

Osteopathic surgeon, Dr. Samuel Sheppard, is found guilty of the brutal murder of his wife in 1954. The prosecution insist that the crime scene had been staged to appear as though burglary was the motive.

Among items supposedly stolen was Dr. Sheppard's wristwatch, but this proves not to be the case as it is subsequently found—with his wife's blood on it. Crime scene photographs depict blood spatters (not smears) which forensic analysis shows to be consistent with impact bloodstains, indicating the watch had been in close proximity to the victim as she was being attacked.

Dr. Sheppard always maintains his innocence and a retrial in 1966 finds him not guilty and sees him set free. But for over fifty years this murder mystery endures—did he or didn't he?

"I WASN'T THERE…"

In 1989, Desmond Applebee is on trial accused of a series of predatory sexual attacks on young women. He is convicted on three counts of sexual assault in Australia's first trial involving DNA evidence. A sample of his blood corresponds to DNA gathered from semen and blood on the clothes of all three victims. In light of these overwhelming serological indicators of his guilt, Applebee is forced to change his defense from "I wasn't there" to "the women consented."

ANALYZING SAMPLES

Microbial forensics includes the entire range of forensic evidence, such as analyses of microbes; materials used to prepare, stabilize and deliver the pathogen or toxin; and fiber, hair, pollen, and fingerprints. Laboratory investigations used in microbial forensics are usually made up from microbiological cultures, molecular sequencing, electron microscopy, biochemistry, mass spectrometry, and crystallography.

These analyses are far more complex than those used for epidemiologic investigations and medical diagnoses, but they do require the same materials such as microbial cultures and body fluid samples. For this reason both the doctor and the laboratory play a vital part in the gathering and analysis of samples for microbial forensics.

THE FIRE AT CHARLES SCHWARTZ'S LAB

On July 30, 1925, a fire destroys the Berkeley, California laboratory of chemist Charles Henry Schwartz. It turns out that Schwartz has tried to fake his own death by attempting to erase identification marks on a corpse in an effort to make it look as if he himself had died.

The fire chief has his doubts. The victim's fingerprints have been destroyed with acid, and the eyes removed. Dental comparisons show that the victim had two missing teeth, as had Schwartz. Dr. Edward Heinrich notes that the dead man's earlobe has a mole on it. Schwartz's did not. The victim had been murdered by Schwartz, who later commits suicide.

LOUISIANA V. SCHMIDT

A good illustration of the microbial forensic system at work is the case of Louisiana v. Schmidt, when HIV-infected blood is used as the weapon in an attempted murder. In the office of the suspect, a gastroenterologist, a vial of HIV-infected blood is discovered. Microbial forensics are asked to provide evidence as to whether this was the source of the victim's HIV infection.

Analysis of blood from the victim, control samples, (i.e., samples from patients with the illness resident in the same geographical area as the victim,) and the vial is performed. These tests prove that the viral RNA from the victim is more closely linked to that from the vial in the suspect's office than to the samples from other patients in the region. This evidence is submitted to the court. The microbial forensics and composite epidemiologic evidence is persuasive and results in a conviction for attempted murder.

JOHN NORMAN COLLINS: LEAVING AN EVIDENTIAL TRAIL

On June 7, 1967, the homicidal John Norman Collins brings Alice Kalom to his apartment. The pair are overheard arguing. Kalom runs from the apartment. According to his roommate, Collins gives chase. When he later returns he is alone. Kalom is discovered murdered, shot in the head and stabbed multiple times. The bullet is from a High Standard revolver which Collins had earlier stolen and the knife wounds are consistent with a hunting knife Collins tried to hide. A boot print on Kalom's skirt matches a boot belonging to Collins. There is also blood found in his car and on a raincoat he owns. Both match Alice Kalom's blood type and the nails begin to be firmly hammered into this sadistic serial killer's coffin.

DEADLY ANNIVERSARY

IT IS A HAPPY OCCASION FOR GIUSEPPINA MARTORANA AND HER HUSBAND GIUSEPPE. THEY ARE ABOUT TO CELEBRATE THEIR TWENTY-FIFTH WEDDING ANNIVERSARY AND THEY'VE BEEN SHOPPING IN LONDON FOR RINGS. THEY STOP FOR A BITE AT MCDONALD'S AND COME TO THE ATTENTION OF DANIEL WHYTE AND JASON JAMES, BECAUSE THE COUPLE ARE WEARING EXPENSIVE ROLEX WATCHES.

THEY ARE FOLLOWED HOME AND, AFTER A FAILED ATTEMPT TO STEAL THE WATCHES, GIUSEPPINA IS SHOT, DYING FROM HER INJURIES A MONTH LATER. HER SON AND HIS GIRLFRIEND ARE ALSO SHOT. MR. MARTORANA ATTEMPTS TO PREVENT THE BOYS' ESCAPE AND RAMS THEIR CAR FROM BEHIND WITH HIS BMW. MONTHS LATER, AN OLD GIRLFRIEND OF JAMES GIVES POLICE A BAG OF CLOTHING. INSIDE IS A DUFFEL COAT AND FORENSIC SCIENTISTS FIND SUBSTANTIAL AMOUNTS OF FIREARMS RESIDUE MATCHING THAT ON GIUSEPPINA. A MIXED PROFILE IS OBTAINED, WHICH MAY CONTAIN DNA FROM JAMES. THIS, ALONG WITH GLASS FOUND EMBEDDED IN THE GETAWAY CAR'S BUMPER THAT IS SIMILAR TO THE BROKEN HEADLAMP FROM THE BMW, IS ENOUGH TO LINK HIM TO THE CRIME. IN MARCH 2002 BOTH JAMES AND WHYTE ARE FOUND GUILTY OF MURDER AND ARE SERVING LIFE SENTENCES.

There is almost too much evidence. Scientists are overwhelmed! In November 2000 police have three dead women, Rosemary Corcoran, Carol Jordan, and Jodie Hyde. Their murders are initially thought to be unconnected but eventually a suspect, Philip Smith, is arrested and two FSS scientists go to his home and one inspects his car. The evidence gathered is vital. The bath contains dismal, brown water full of seemingly bloodstained clothes, and this becomes the first of many links between the three victims and the suspect. Others include:

a) In the house:

Pink fibers (also present in the car) matching the blanket wrapped around Jodie Hyde's body;

Blood matching all three victims;

Ladies' trousers linked by DNA to Rosemary Corcoran.

b) In the car:

Paint which matches that on Carol Jordan's trousers;

The mud flap, one wing and a tire are smeared with Rosemary Corcoran's blood;

A bloody fingerprint discovered on a back window proves a DNA match to Rosemary Corcoran;

Blood found on a headrest belongs to Jodie Hyde;

Pattern elements from tire impressions matches marks on one of Rosemary Corcoran's arms.

The work of the forensic scientists gives police a powerful case against Smith and he is jailed for life at Leicester Crown Court in August 2001.

WOMAN IN A SUITCASE

THE GRIM DISCOVERY OF THE BODY OF A WOMAN IN A SUITCASE IS MADE. IT IS 1991 AND AN ANTHROPOLOGIST AND THE FSS USING RED HAIR ANALYSIS AS AN ETHNIC MARKER, CONFIRM THE WOMAN TO BE SOUTHEAST ASIAN (ORIENTAL). INFORMATION REGARDING FINGERPRINTS, DNA AND DENTAL RECORDS EVENTUALLY IDENTIFIES THE VICTIM AS HYO JUNG JIN, ORIGINALLY FROM KOREA; SHE HAS BEEN STAYING TEMPORARILY AT AN ADDRESS IN LONDON. HER MURDER IS SOON LINKED WITH ANOTHER KOREAN STUDENT, HEA SONG, WHOSE BODY WAS FOUND IN A CUPBOARD.

THE LANDLORD OF BOTH PROPERTIES IS THIRTY-ONE-YEAR-OLD KYO SOO KIM. FSS EXPERTS PRODUCE A RANGE OF EVIDENCE. THE TAPE USED TO ASPHYXIATE THE STUDENT HAS AN UNUSUAL PATTERN; A ROLL IS FOUND AT KIM'S LONDON ADDRESS. ORANGE PAINT FOUND ON THE TAPE MATCHES THAT ON A T-SHIRT BELONGING TO KIM. HYO JUNG JIN'S BLOOD IS FOUND ON THE CARPET, BED, WALLS, AND SKIRTING BOARDS, AND ALSO IN THE TRUNK OF KIM'S CAR. BLUE PAINT FROM A BEDROOM WALL MATCHES PAINT PRESENT ON THE SUITCASE. IN 2003 KIM GOES TO TRIAL AT THE OLD BAILEY. HE IS FOUND GUILTY.

THE SCARF, THE TIES, AND THE DOG

Sixteen-year-old Leanne Tiernan's badly decomposed body holds all the clues, but it takes FSS scientists from many different fields of specialty to work together to bring her killer to justice. Leanne's brutalized body had been wrapped in green refuse sacks, a black plastic bag secured by a dog collar encased her head, a scarf held by green twine was around her neck, and the same type of twine bound her wrists. If the body were not so badly decomposed it would have been considerably easier to draw physical evidence; however, the state of decomposition contaminates the results. Scientists use the method of Mitochondrial DNA to crack the case.

The knot in the scarf contains hairs that, when tested at the root, prove inconclusive, but when Mitochondrial DNA testing is used on the small samples found in the shaft of the hair, they are matched to forty-six-year-old John Taylor. The twine is a special type made in Devon as "rabbit netting"—only a small amount was ever sold, but the manufacturer remembers selling some to Taylor. Dog hairs that are found on the body are sent to a Texan university that runs a program of identifying dog DNA. A partial profile is built but cannot be used as the dog that Taylor owned at the time of her abduction and murder has since died. However, along with information from the manufacturer of the dog collar, this evidence convicts Taylor of the murders and he is sentenced to life imprisonment.

MUCH EVIDENCE...

Neighbors are concerned and police break into the home of fifty-year-old Michael Reaney. He has been bound, gagged, and assaulted. He is also dead. His flat is a shambles and various items have been stolen. The Metropolitan Police soon have a pair of suspects— Francis Carbon and Andrew Docherty, already thought responsible for a series of aggravated robberies, many of which are at small supermarkets in South London. About three hundred and sixty items taken from their homes are sent for forensic testing; these include black gaffer tape and a stereo.

The scientist leading the biological investigation is able to find a variety of connections between the crime and the suspects: blood on Carbon's crash helmet, handgun, and trainers come from two victims. Fingerprints on the stereo belong to both Carbon and Docherty. On the black tape is found blood from an armed robbery victim, and fibers on the tape covering Michael's mouth match those found on Carbon's glove. There is much more. It takes forty-five minutes to read out all the charges in court. The two men are jailed for a total of twenty-six years for manslaughter, robbery, and firearm charges.

Kevin Jackson gives chase to three men attempting to steal his father-in-law's car. He is stabbed in the head with a screwdriver, dying two days afterward. A few days later police arrest Rashad Zaman; his car is examined and a screwdriver, which turns out to be the murder weapon, is found in the trunk. Microscopic traces of blood on the screwdriver are analyzed and found to match the victim. Marks on the lock of the car the gang had been trying to steal are proved to have been made by the screwdriver. Rangzaib Akhtar and Raees Khan are apprehended three weeks after the attack and their homes searched.

A pair of boots found at Zaman's house are covered in spatters of Kevin Jackson's blood—the spatters proving the wearer had been in close proximity to the attack. Another expert examines footwear prints made in the snow at the scene. These are matched to trainers found at Akhtar's home.

A vital piece of evidence is skin scrapings taken from under Kevin Jackson's fingernails. A full DNA profile is developed and loaded on the National DNA Database. A match to Khan is made. The three men, all from Bradford, England, are found guilty of murder in December 2002 at Leeds Crown Court; each receives life imprisonment.

FOUND GUILTY

ALTHOUGH FOUND GUILTY AND SENTENCED TO A MINIMUM OF EIGHTEEN YEARS, OWEN ANDERSON VEHEMENTLY DENIES THE MURDER OF GARY LINN IN AUGUST 2001. LINN, A SALESMAN FROM KILSYTH, SCOTLAND, HAD BEEN KILLED BY REPEATED BLOWS TO THE HEAD WITH A HAMMER OR SOMETHING SIMILAR. HIS BODY HAD BEEN FOUND, NINE MONTHS AFTER HE WENT MISSING, IN A RIVER IN MIDLOTHIAN. AT THE SUSPECT'S HOME, BLOOD SPOTS WERE DISCOVERED IN THE KITCHEN AND BATHROOM, ON THE FLOOR AND WALL, AND EVEN UNDER THE FLOOR.

A FORENSIC SCIENTIST SAID DNA EXTRACTED FROM OVER TWENTY BLOODSTAINS AND SPOTS MATCHED MR. LINN'S PARENTS. THE ODDS AGAINST THESE NOT BELONGING TO LINN WERE ONE IN FOURTEEN MILLION. A FORENSIC PATHOLOGIST FROM EDINBURGH UNIVERSITY SAYS THE ATTACK HAD BEEN PARTICULARLY VICIOUS AND THE SEVERE DAMAGE TO THE FRONT OF THE SKULL MAY HAVE BEEN AN ENDEAVOR TO ERASE THE FACIAL FEATURES TO MAKE IDENTIFICATION IMPOSSIBLE.

Professor Francis Crick, of Northampton, U.K., and American James Watson both unlocked the key of life in 1953. The scientists, along with Maurice Wilkins, were awarded a Nobel Prize in 1962 for discovering the double helix structure of DNA.

A steel sculpture called Discovery is installed in Abington Street, Northampton. It is more than twenty-six feet tall and includes two life-size figures.

Lynn Wilson, chair of the Wilson Foundation, says: "The sculpture celebrates the life of a world-class scientist who must surely be considered the greatest Northamptonian of all time."

Professor Watson is chancellor and former president of Cold Spring Harbor Laboratory, Indiana.

DNA INHERITANCE

When a child is born it inherits half of its DNA and chromosomes from each parent. The child's DNA "fingerprint" will match its parents exactly. Even different offspring of the same couple will share the same relationship with their parents' DNA. This means that DNA samples can be positively identified by testing them against known relatives or descendents generations—or even centuries—later. DNA researchers have even been able to identify DNA from the bodies of mummified Egyptian pharaohs that are thousands of years old.

DEFENDING A DNA MATCH

"If there is a match it doesn't mean they did the crime," says James Walker, the laboratory manager at University Diagnostics Ltd, a DNA laboratory working for defense lawyers. "It just means they were at the scene at some point in time. The person is a suspect, and there has to be other evidence. Also the fingerprint is not unique, somebody could have a profile with a frequency of one in three million but in a population of sixty million that means there could be twenty others with the same fingerprint." In dealing with semen swabs, which can contain victim's cells, he says, "If it is from a crime scene, bacteria and yeasts could have degraded the DNA. If the sample wasn't clean then it is important to check."

SEMEN

Semen stains are the most common source rendered for DNA analysis but they are also tested by more conventional methods before DNA analysis. Microscopy and sperm cell specific staining can decide whether or not the stain has leaked from the vagina. Post-coital drainage will comprise both vaginal and sperm cells. Dried semen stains on clothing or furniture can still be detected after many years. Sperm can be present in the vagina for more than three days so in rape cases the victim's boyfriend/sexual partner should also be tested.

BLOOD

Bloodstains may come from more than one person, thereby providing more complicated DNA profiles, but using DNA testing is really the only method of finding out whether the stain is a mixture of two different individuals. It can also determine if the individuals are of the same sex. Gender is the only physical characteristic that can be established in this way.

EXEMPLARS

Samples taken from victims or suspects usually consist of liquid blood and are called exemplars. These are the easiest and most dependable of blood specimens. The best way to preserve the samples is to freeze them. They are normally handled as a group of dime-sized stains on clean cotton sheets, making storage and transportation simple.

BUCCAL SWABS

A non-invasive method of obtaining exemplars is to take buccal swabs, i.e., from inside the check. These are used if an individual cannot give blood samples because of medical or religious reasons.

PURIFYING THE SPECIMEN

The successful testing of a sample can be deeply affected by the surface on which it is found. It is simple enough to extract DNA from dried blood from, for example, light cloth, hard plastic, metal, and glass. More difficult and requiring extra processes are samples from, e.g., carpet, vinyl, denim, vehicle seats, and other heavily colored and thick fibers.

In these cases the DNA testing methods need to "purify" the specimen by excluding any other substances contained in the sample. Porous products such as concrete make the blood very difficult to separate and it is practically impossible to obtain DNA from soil.

SALIVA

DNA can be obtained from bottles, cups, telephone mouthpieces, cigarette butts discarded at crime scenes—even bite marks and penile swabs. It can also be extracted from saliva found on stamps or gummed envelope flaps—this was the done in the World Trade Center investigation.

HAIR ROOTS

Once shed, hairs will provide only slight traces of DNA and are not a particularly good source for routine forensic use. But one to five hair roots can contain sufficient for RFLP analysis. Mitochondrial sequencing is being increasingly used in hair analysis as well.

TISSUES

At autopsy the extraction of DNA from tissues is an easy process. Mostly soft tissues are isolated from partially decomposed bodies. DNA survives longest in teeth and bone, a little less long in brain and muscle, and only for a relatively short time in, for example, kidney and liver. Sometimes enough DNA for testing can come from tiny amounts of, say, brain tissue, dispersed by gunshot or on the gun itself, or on a recovered bullet.

CHEMICALLY TREATED TISSUES

The normal chemical treatments for preserving bodies are embalming and formaldehyde fixation. Both types of tissues yield samples appropriate for DNA testing—even bodies that have been buried for many years. Exhumations are regularly performed to extract a known exemplar to compare with forensic evidence in murder cases.

MATHEMATICS AND FREQUENCY

In order to give an estimate of how common a genetic profile he has developed might be found in population groups, the forensic scientist will use mathematics. If the genetic profiles found in two different specimens—one from a suspect and one from a piece of evidence—and they cannot be differentiated, this is called "a match."

A USEFUL ILLUSTRATION

DNA typing is a complicated process, and a good analogy is to compare the method by which genetic data is stored in DNA and the manner in which data is stored in books. The illustration given uses the *Encyclopaedia Britannica*: if we take the first forty volumes, cut up all the sentences, and glue them together end to end, then we have all the information equivalent to what is stored in the DNA that is found in every cell that makes up our bodies. In fact the physical formation of the data, the long continuous strip of paper, would be in the same form as the DNA information contained within our bodies.

DRAWING THE UNLUCKY STRAW

A woman's body is found just outside Syracuse, New York, in 1975. She has been raped and stabbed. Next to her lies the business card of Donald Sigsbee. Police are unable to link him directly to the murder but he remains their chief suspect for several years. This is all before the advent of DNA, but a forensic scientist at the time of the murder isolates a sample of semen from the scene of the crime and stores it as a microscope slide. In 2003 Sigsbee throws away a drinking straw and seals his fate. His DNA profile matches the preserved evidence. Justice was a long time coming for the family of the murdered woman.

ORTHODOX BLOOD TYPING

IN ORTHODOX BLOOD TYPING FOR A TYPICAL POPULATION GROUP THE FREQUENCY COULD BE ONE IN TWO HUNDRED; USE DNA TYPING AND THE FIGURE WOULD BE ONE IN FIVE MILLION. IN OTHER WORDS ONLY ONE IN FIVE MILLION PEOPLE WOULD HAVE AN IDENTICAL DNA PROFILE. ONCE THE REPORT REGARDING FREQUENCY IS SUBMITTED, THEN THE DECISION ON WHETHER THE DEFENDANT IS INNOCENT OR GUILTY IS UP TO THE COURT. THE REPORT WILL, OF COURSE, BE CONSIDERED, BUT THE OTHER EVIDENCE CONCERNING THE CRIME, FOR EXAMPLE, MOTIVE, INTENTION, MEANS, AND OPPORTUNITY WILL ALSO BE JUDGED.

A SEXUAL ASSAULT ON A FEMALE PROFESSOR TOOK PLACE IN MARCH 2000 ON A COLLEGE CAMPUS, WHERE A FEMALE PROFESSOR HAD BEEN PREVIOUSLY ASSAULTED IN 1987. LAMONT COLEMAN, A CRIMINAL WITH A HISTORY OF SEX OFFENCES, WAS FOUND GUILTY OF THE 1987 MURDER AND HIS DNA PROFILE WAS LOADED ONTO THE STATE'S DNA DATABANK. PHYSICAL EVIDENCE COLLECTED AT THE SCENE OF THE 2000 ASSAULT MATCHED COLEMAN'S PROFILE. HE REMAINED A FUGITIVE ON THE FBI'S "MOST WANTED" LIST FOR TWO YEARS BEFORE HE WAS APPREHENDED IN JULY 2002.

WELL WORTH SAMPLING

In 1979 a twenty-two-year-old woman was viciously stabbed to death in Westchester County. While committing the murder her attacker had apparently cut himself. Bloodstains found at the time were stored until DNA testing could take place in 2000.

A match is found from the resulting DNA profile with one in the state's DNA Databank from Walter Gill, who is currently in jail for robbery which, until a 1999 amendment to the DNA Database law, did not require DNA sampling. Gill was found guilty of manslaughter in the first degree.

FIRST BLOOD

A young financial analyst, on her way to work one morning in October 2000, is dragged into a freight elevator and brutally choked, beaten, and raped. The plucky young woman fights back and bites her attacker, drawing some blood, which falls onto her jacket later retained as crucial evidence. From the bloodstain a DNA profile is developed and loaded onto the DNA Database. There is a "hit" against the profile of Richard Navas. He is found guilty of rape in the first degree and assault.

LOADED ONTO THE DATABASE

Celebrations for the Fourth of July are taking place in 1992 in Madison County. A fifteen-year-old boy leaves the restaurant where he works to join his parents at a carnival. It is only a five-minute walk, but during that time he is abducted, sexually assaulted, and murdered.

There are a great many transient people in town that weekend because of the celebrations and police follow up hundreds of leads. In 2000 Jeffrey Clark is convicted of sodomy and his DNA profile is loaded onto the DNA Database. In 2001 forensic evidence collected from the fifteen-year-old is found to match Clark's profile. No contest: he pleads guilty to the 1992 murder.

NOT CAREFUL ENOUGH

It is 1998 in New York City and a female employee of a large department store has gone into the stock room to fetch a dress. An unknown assailant follows her in and chokes and rapes her. The woman manages to prick the man with her employee badge and he bleeds onto the dress and the floor. The attacker then runs away, taking care to hide his face from the security camera.

In 2002 Joe Felder provides a DNA sample when he commits a burglary and the profile produced from the bloodstain matches his profile. He is convicted of rape in the first degree.

MUCH OBLIGED

An intruder breaks into the home of an eighty-year-old woman in Onondaga County in 1999. He proceeds to rape and sodomize her. Try as she might, the unfortunate victim cannot identify her attacker. At the scene, forensic evidence is isolated and the DNA profile entered into the DNA Databank. It matches the profile of Sean Coyne who, it transpires, is on probation for a second attempted robbery. Because of the 1999 amendments to the DNA Database law, he had been obliged to provide a DNA sample.

POSITIVE HIT COMES BACK TO HAUNT

ROMMAL BENNETT PLEADS GUILTY IN 2004 TO THE 1986 MURDER OF THE PROPRIETOR OF A DINER IN MONTICELLO, SO ENDING A NEARLY EIGHTEEN-YEAR-OLD MYSTERY. A HIT ON THE NATIONAL DNA DATABASE SYSTEM LINKS BENNETT TO A PROFILE DEVELOPED FROM A CIGARETTE BUTT FOUND IN A BOTTLE OF BEER IN THE VICTIM'S HOME. BENNETT'S DNA PROFILE HAS BEEN LOADED ONTO THE DATABASE BY THE FORENSIC LABORATORY IN MINNESOTA BECAUSE OF A SEXUAL OFFENCE HE COMMITTED IN 1994.

NAZI DOCTOR OF DEATH FINALLY FOUND

Following WWII, the allies want to bring all of the top Nazi war criminals to justice. Many escape to South America. One such Nazi is Dr. Josef Mengele, who is responsible for the deaths of thousands of concentration camp inmates at Auschwitz, many of them children, through carrying out horrifying and barbarous experiments upon them. In the mid 1980s it is alleged that Mengele has died in Brazil and is buried under the name of Wolfgang Gerhard. The grave is exhumed but the body cannot be definitely identified as Mengele. Not until 1992, when DNA samples are taken from Mengele's living relatives in Germany and compared to the corpse, is the body finally confirmed as that of Mengele.

REOPENING THE CASE

In 1967, a twelve-year-old boy named Keith Lyon is stabbed to death on the Sussex Downs, Southeast England.

It is among the largest murder investigations ever seen in Sussex, with fingerprints taken from more than five thousand youths. Police find a bloodstained knife at a nearby school along with blood in a toilet block sink. This is mislaid, but decades later, in 2002, is found by chance in an evidence box by contractors upgrading the sprinkler system at Brighton Police Station. Forensic technology will now be applied to test the bloodstains on the knife. Police are trying to trace a family who emigrated to Canada after the tragedy.

EXONERATED BY DNA

Gary Dotson has the dubious honor of being the first person to be exonerated by DNA evidence in the U.S. In 1979 he is found guilty of rape and aggravated kidnapping and sentenced to two terms of twenty-five to fifty years to be served concurrently. In 1985, the accusing witness, whose testimony had been the main evidence against Dotson, recants. However he is not exonerated at this time but, aided by popular belief that he is a victim of a false rape accusation, and enduring a string of paroles and reincarcerations, DNA evidence finally confirms his innocence and he is released in 1988.

BLOODSWORTH WALKS

KIRK BLOODSWORTH IS SENTENCED TO DEATH IN MARYLAND IN 1984 FOR THE SEXUAL ASSAULT, MUTILATION AND MURDER OF A NINE-YEAR-OLD GIRL. ONLY EYE-WITNESS TESTIMONY AND AN ANONYMOUS TIP-OFF HAD PLACED HIM AT THE SCENE OF THE CRIME—THERE IS NO PHYSICAL EVIDENCE, AND HE PROTESTS HIS INNOCENCE.

BLOODSWORTH HAD BECOME AWARE OF DNA PROFILING WHILE IN PRISON. WITH THE ASSISTANCE OF HIS LAWYER

AND A NONPROFIT LEGAL CLINIC CREATED TO ENCOURAGE THE USE OF DNA ANALYSIS IN THE EXONERATION OF INNOCENT PRISONERS, THE INNOCENCE PROJECT, OFFICIALS ARE PERSUADED TO COMPARE DRIED SPERM FOUND ON THE CHILD WITH BLOODSWORTH'S DNA. THERE IS NO MATCH AND BLOODSWORTH IS EXONERATED—THE FIRST DEATH ROW PRISONER TO BE FREED BECAUSE OF POSTCONVICTION DNA TESTING.

PITCHFORK FAILS HIS TEST

Two teenage girls are murdered in 1983 and 1986 respectively. Semen analysis from both crime scenes determines that they had been killed by the same person. The prime suspect, a local man named Richard Buckland, confesses to the second murder, but police are convinced he killed both girls. However, using a blood sample from Buckland and DNA profiles of crime scene stains, it is conclusively proved that the perpetrator was not Buckland. Thus he is the first person in the world to be exonerated of murder through the use of DNA evidence.

A DNA mass intelligence screen then takes place but no match is found. That is until it is established that Colin Pitchfork, a local baker, had persuaded somebody else to take the test for him. He is arrested and his sample matches the profile. He is subsequently sentenced to life imprisonment for both homicides.

PRECIOUS FLUIDS

THE UNKNOWN SOLDIER

The remains of a soldier killed during the Vietnam War are buried in the Tomb of the Unknowns at Arlington National Cemetery in 1984. Ten years later the identity of this Unknown Soldier is being questioned. In 1972 First Lieutenant Michael Blassie was shot down over South Vietnam. His family, after being advised that his remains might be interred in the Tomb of the Unknowns, procures an exhumation. The damaged bones undergo mitochondrial DNA testing by forensic anthropologists. The mtDNA is passed along the maternal line and the investigators compare samples taken from Blassie's sister and mother with the Unknown Soldier's DNA and find a match.

FAMILY TIES

Russell Bradbury pleads guilty, at Newcastle Crown Court, to the 1986 rape of a twenty-two-year-old woman in Killingworth, North Tyneside, U.K. Twenty years after the crime a new DNA technique known as "familial searching" is used by Northumbria Police to link him to the crime scene. DNA evidence from the victim procures a partial match with profiles of close relatives of Bradbury on the database. Swabbing determines a full match with Bradbury. Assistant Chief Constable Kevin Mathieson says: "It's extremely satisfying to know that a rapist has been taken off the streets because of our commitment to using pioneering technology in detecting unsolved crimes and the excellent work of our partners in the Forensic Science Service."

In 1982, during a robbery in a photography studio in Buffalo, an eighty-four-year-old woman is strangled and a fifty-four-year-old man shot dead. While the robbery is taking place, the proprietor of the studio and six other customers who come in are bound and robbed. One of the surviving victims is raped and sodomized. Caustic solution is splashed into all the victims' eyes, apparently in an attempt to blind them, thereby making them unable to identify the criminal.

From evidence collected from the victim who had been sexually assaulted, forensic scientists are able to construct the criminal's DNA profile. Less than a year later Ishmael Saladeen is found guilty of two counts of attempted murder in the second degree and is sentenced to a long term in prison.

A DNA sample was collected from him and found to match the perpetrator of the 1982 sexual assault. Unfortunately, due to the Statute of Limitations, Saladeen could not be indicted on rape and sodomy charges but, because he was linked to the photography studio crime scene through the sexual assault evidence, he is found guilty of murder in the second degree.

THE WRONG MAN

A seventeen-year-old girl is robbed, raped, and sodomized in New York City in 1991. At the time DNA science is still limited and the rape kit yields no DNA evidence. However, a man is convicted of the crime and sentenced to twenty to forty years in jail. New DNA technology later makes possible a new test on the evidence and a profile is developed and loaded onto the Databank.

When the DNA profile of the convicted man is compared to the evidence from the crime it is determined that the man had not been the perpetrator. Instead it matches another prison inmate. This is another illustration of the fact that DNA evidence, in addition to incriminating the guilty, can also exonerate the innocent.

BY THE SKIN OF HIS TEETH

In Austin, Texas, a student is raped and choked with a phone cord. It is possible to obtain DNA evidence from a ligature because skin cells rub off the perpetrator's hands as he tries to pull the cord with sufficient force, thus creating friction. Anticipating this, the rapist wears gloves, but during the assault is obliged to use one hand to hold the struggling victim, leaving only one to pull the cord tight. He is forced to pull the other end with his teeth and hence leaves saliva on the cord. Ironically his DNA profile is obtained from saliva rather than skin.

CRIME DOESN'T PAY

As a woman walks home from her job in Manhattan in 1999 she is grabbed by a man who threatens to kill her. He pulls her into a stairwell and proceeds to rape her. By promising him money she entices him to an ATM machine, where she hopes the security camera has captured his face on film. The attacker is not identified from the photo, but two months later Lashange Legrand is on parole for attempted robbery and, a DNA sample is taken. When it is loaded onto the DNA Databank it scores a "hit" with the DNA profile developed from forensic evidence isolated from the earlier attack. Faced with the evidence, Legrand pleads guilty to rape and off he goes to jail again.

TOMMY LEE ANDREWS—ONE OF THE FIRST

It is November 1987, and in an Orange County, Florida, courtroom, Tommy Lee Andrews stands accused of raping a woman. After DNA tests match his DNA from a blood sample with that of semen traces found in the rape victim, he is convicted. It is one of the first uses of DNA in a criminal case in the United States.

WEST VIRGINIA SUPREME COURT V. GLEN WOODALL

On July 8, 1987, a jury finds Glen Woodall guilty of robbing, raping, and kidnapping two women. He is sentenced by the circuit court to two life terms without parole and to 203–335 years in prison. West Virginia Supreme Court is the first State High Court to rule on the admissibility of DNA evidence. The court accepts DNA testing by the defendant, but inconclusive results fail to exculpate Woodall. The court upholds the conviction. Subsequent DNA testing determines that Woodall was innocent.

DNA CATCHES UP

Twenty-two-year-old Lorraine Benson is murdered over the Christmas period, 1988, in Southwest London. It is a "stranger" attack which will be solved by DNA. Scotland Yard's DNA unit analyzes traces of saliva found at the scene. A man's handkerchief also found at the scene contains Lorraine Benson's blood.

John Dunne is arrested for attempted rape in February 1989. A sample of DNA is taken from him and analyzed by the laboratory. Mucus on the handkerchief matches his DNA. There is only a one in 1,497,000 chance that he had not been at the scene of Lorraine's murder. Dunne confesses and is sentenced to life imprisonment.

"I'LL BE BACK!"

In May 1989 "Anne" (name changed) is at home in Williamsburg, Virginia. Unknown to her a masked man has entered the house and she is grabbed, blindfolded, and dragged to a wooded area. Her attacker robs her, rapes her several times, and threatens to come back for her if she tells anybody. But she does tell her husband and he convinces her to go to the police, where she is examined and physical evidence is collected. Six years later a forensic scientist informs "Anne" that a DNA match has been made with an inmate of a Virginia prison. She can at long last stop living in fear.

GIVING THEM A NAME

It has always been a priority for the U.S. government to swiftly and accurately identify the men and women who lose their lives serving in the armed forces. But not all remains can be identified using dental records, fingerprints, etc. DNA analysis has now become the most important of forensic technologies and in 1991 the Armed Forces DNA Identification Laboratory (AFDIL) is formed and uses DNA analysis to identify at least one hundred and fifty military personnel from World War II, Korea, and Vietnam. Now everyone who enlists in the U.S. forces has DNA samples taken. It is hoped that this will ensure a much enhanced chance at identifying their remains should they die during the call of duty.

THE NIGHT STALKER

IN 1990 AN UNIDENTIFIED PERPETRATOR KNOWN ONLY AS THE "NIGHT STALKER" (NOT TO BE CONFUSED WITH SERIAL KILLER RICHARD RAMIREZ) BEGINS A SERIES OF VIOLENT ASSAULTS AND RAPES ON ELDERLY VICTIMS IN NORTH CAROLINA. HIS THIRD ATTACK RESULTS IN THE MURDERS OF AN OLD COUPLE AND, IN AN EFFORT TO CONCEAL THE CRIME, HE SETS THEIR HOUSE ON FIRE.

DNA SAMPLE GATHERED FROM VAGINAL SWABS TAKEN FROM EACH RAPE VICTIM PROVE THE SAME MAN IS RESPONSIBLE BUT POLICE HAVE NO SUSPECT. A DECADE LATER, WITH THE EMERGENCE OF IMPROVED TECHNOLOGY, THE EVIDENCE IS RETESTED AND THE DNA PROFILE COMPARED TO THOUSANDS OF OFFENDER PROFILES.

IN 2001 A "COLD HIT" TO THE DATABASE RESULTS IN A MATCH AND THE SUSPECT ADMITS TO ALL THREE CRIMES.

MARK NELSON, SPECIAL AGENT IN CHARGE OF THE NORTH CAROLINA STATE CRIME LABORATORY, SAYS, "EVEN THOUGH THESE TERRIBLE CRIMES OCCURRED MORE THAN TEN YEARS AGO, WE NEVER GAVE UP HOPE OF SOLVING THEM ONE DAY."

On April 27, 1994, predatory serial sex killer Timothy Wilson Spencer is executed in Virginia's electric chair. DNA evidence sent him there. The multiple rape-murders he committed throughout the 1980s were the first cases in the United States where the admission of DNA evidence led to guilty verdicts and secured Spencer his death sentence.

The Virginia Supreme Court upholds the murder and rape convictions of Spencer, after finding that testing matched his DNA with that of semen found in several victims. The defendant attempts, unsuccessfully, to suppress the introduction of DNA evidence at his trial, and Timothy Spencer is subsequently consigned to oblivion for his heinous misdeeds.

BUT AT WHAT COST TO THE VICTIM?

Everything changes for "Carol" (name changed) one night in 1994 in Florida. She is in the laundry room of her apartment complex when she is viciously attacked by a man who beats and rapes her. She has no qualms about reporting her ordeal despite being "plucked and scraped and swabbed," and forensic scientists are able to retrieve a semen sample from her clothing. But due to funding issues the authorities sit on her DNA evidence for more than three years before it is analyzed. Her rapist's DNA profile matches that of a man already serving a twenty-five year sentence for beating and raping a woman six weeks before his assault on "Carol."

THE DNA REVOLUTION

In 1995 Ricky McGinn receives the death sentence for the May 1993 rape and slaying of his stepdaughter. He claims he is innocent. During autopsy a single pubic hair is found in the girl's vagina, but DNA testing, due to its relative infancy, cannot render the test conclusive. Things move on, however, and more advanced DNA testing is performed on the pubic hair and on a semen stain found on the victim. The tests are positive and McGinn is later convicted and, after spending some five years awaiting his fate on Death Row, is executed on September 27, 2000.

LEFT BEHIND AT THE SCENE

In 1995, a sixty-six-year-old widow is murdered; the killer decides to leave his own excrement at the crime scene. At the time DNA profiling techniques are limited and are only able to establish that the feces were not the victim's; one of the suspects is eliminated.

In 2001 the material is examined again and checked against the National DNA Database—it matches with a sample taken from John Cook, who is later convicted. This is the first occasion when a full DNA profile has been obtained from human feces.

CRIMINAL DNA

IN 1995, AFTER SOME PAINSTAKING COLLATION, THE FIRST DATABASE OF CRIMINALS' DNA IS ESTABLISHED BY THE FORENSIC SCIENCE SERVICE. IN FOUR YEARS' TIME MATCHES BETWEEN CRIME SCENES AND SUSPECTS HAVE REACHED APPROXIMATELY FIVE HUNDRED PER WEEK. MANY OF THESE CONCERN DECEPTION, BURGLARY, AND OTHER CRIMES NOT NECESSARILY INVOLVING VIOLENCE.

A PAIR OF SUNGLASSES CATCH A RAPIST

In 2005 Duncan Turner rapes a woman but leaves behind a pair of sunglasses. This oversight will eventually lead to the end of an eighteen-year career of sex crime. When the sunglasses are sent for forensic examination two DNA sources are found to be blended together. Experts use new techniques to separate the DNA. Turner's details are in the National Database and this assists them in identifying him. Forensic scientist Kate Jones tells the Press: "I hope this shows we are constantly coming up with new techniques to look at DNA and utilizing the DNA database in different ways.

"I hope it sends out a message—that we are going to find them eventually."

MISTAKEN IDENTITY

In 1999, a U.K. police agency matches a sample taken from the scene of a burglary to six loci on the DNA molecule of one of the seven hundred thousand people whose DNA has been collected in the National Database. The suspect lives two hundred miles away from the scene and suffers from advanced Parkinson's disease. In spite of the provision of an alibi and his protests of innocence, he is arrested because the DNA matches. Further testing, using additional markers, is done after the suspect has been in jail for several months. The original interpretation is proved to be inaccurate and the prisoner freed. The odds against a suspect's DNA being wrongly matched against the crime scene are estimated to be one in thirty-seven million.

ONE DRINK TOO MANY

In the early hours of an August 1999 morning, a University of Virginia student awakes with a gun pointed at her head. After raping her, the intruder blindfolds her and leads her around the house looking for things to steal. He forces her to shower in order to destroy any physical evidence.
He helps himself to a beer and leaves, not realizing that enough body fluids (including those on the beer can) still remain to link him to the crime. The police draw up a suspect list but there are no DNA matches. Six weeks later a match is made to Montaret Davis who is already resident at the Albermarle Charlottesville Regional Jail.

MITOCHONDRIAL DNA

WHEREAS RACIAL ORIGIN CAN OFTEN BE GUESSED AT IN A COUNTRY SUCH AS CANADA, THIS CAN BE DIFFICULT WHERE MANY PEOPLE ARE OF MIXED DESCENT. USING A HAIR WITH A FOLLICULAR TAG—MEANING IT WAS PULLED OUT—DNA STUDY IS POSSIBLE AND IS A METHOD OF DETERMINING A GENETIC PROFILE. IF THERE IS NO FOLLICULAR TAG PRESENT, MITOCHONDRIAL DNA ANALYSIS IS AN ALTERNATIVE. MITOCHONDRIAL DNA ANALYSIS CAN CREATE A PROFILE OF GENETIC MATERIAL SOLELY FROM A PERSON'S MOTHER. IT CANNOT BE USED TO DISTINGUISH BETWEEN SIBLINGS.

FBI HAIR STUDY

In the course of further broadening the sphere of forensic evidence which can be used for important analytical purposes, the FBI conducts a study of hair evidence. Eleven percent of hairs deemed to be matches upon visual inspection subsequently prove not to match after DNA testing.

The new form of evidence known as mitochondrial DNA first sets its precedent in 1996 when it helps bring the murderer of a four-year-old Tennessee girl to justice. After a night of heavy drinking, Paul Ware wakes up in bed next to the cold body of the little girl, from whose parents he rents a room.

He claims to have no recollection of the previous night and although the girl has been raped and brutally murdered no semen is found on her and none of her blood is on Ware. However, during the autopsy, a ginger hair that matches Ware's is found deep within the girl's throat. Due to this mitochondrial DNA evidence he is found guilty of murder and sentenced to life.

RIPPER HOAXER HUMBLED BY DNA

The hunt for the Yorkshire Ripper is one of Britain's largest manhunts. In the late 1970s the "Ripper Squad" and the media receive a series of hoax letters and tapes claiming to be from the killer. The voice heard on the tape has a distinctive "Geordie" (Newcastle) accent. The hoax is of such a quality that police mistakenly believe that the killer does not have a Yorkshire accent and they misdirect the entire investigation, allowing the real Ripper to claim further victims.

Nearly thirty years later scientists test tiny segments of the envelopes with a technique known as Low Copy Number (LCN) DNA and are able to produce a reliable profile. It is from this profile that "Wearside Jack," as he is labeled, is identified as John Humble from Northumbria. Humble is sentenced to eight years in prison for perverting the course of justice.

CATCHING UP WITH THE M25 RAPIST

The attacks begin in November 2001 in Ashford, Kent, Southwest London. A ten-year-old girl is abducted, assaulted and raped. A DNA profile is obtained from evidence at the scene but no match is found. Eight months later in Surrey, a thirty-year-old woman out walking is beaten and raped. The DNA profile matches the one from the previous attack.

This is seen as a breakthrough by the Forensic Science Service (FSS). A specialist adviser says, "These two assaults would never have been linked through traditional policing methods, the rape of a ten-year-old and a thirty-year-old in different counties with different M.O.s." After three further attacks police still fail to get a match despite screening a thousand men viewed as suspects.

Eventually a fourteen-year-old girl, raped in Hertfordshire, assists police in compiling a picture of her attacker, which leads them to Antoni Imiela. Two days after supplying a DNA sample he abducts and assaults another ten-year-old child. The sample he provides matches the DNA profile from the first assault and he is sentenced to life in March 2004.

FROM THE ASHES

A project called "Operation Phoenix" is looking at all unsolved sexual offences over the period 1985–1999. Northumberland police have enlisted the help of scientists at the FSS (Forensic Science Service) to reinvestigate sex crimes. The project is utilizing previously unavailable DNA techniques such as DNA Low Copy Number (DNA LCN) and FSS SGMplus (a DNA technique used by FSS) to create DNA profiles which couldn't be obtained before or where the methods used were not compatible with the National DNA Database.

One of the success stories is that of Mark Wilkinson from Sunderland. Investigations carried out by the FSS reanalyzed samples from original swabs taken from a nineteen-year-old rape victim some seven years previously. A match is made to Wilkinson and he is imprisoned in January 2003 for five years.

AN INTUITIVE APPROACH

An inspired hunch by FSS scientists leads to the development of a killer's profile though evidence is apparently left. Geraldine Palk had been murdered in 1991; the FSS's specialist DNA unit is attempting to obtain a profile of her killer from the plastic tube used as a repository for medical swabs collected from her body over a decade previously. As the earlier investigations performed had utilized all the evidence, forensic scientists decide to test the plastic receptacle the swabs had been stored in. They are hopeful that traces from the cotton wool swab still remain on the inside of the tube. The tip of the swab stick is also examined.

Astonishingly, a complete DNA profile is obtained and on the national DNA Database it matches the profile of Mark Hampson. He is found guilty of murder and jailed for life.

NO HIDING PLACE

It is 1999 and Brian Lunn Field from the West Midlands, England, is charged with drink driving. A routine DNA buccal swab is obtained and loaded onto the National DNA Database. This drunken act will cost him his freedom for a very long time.

Roy Tuthill, a missing fourteen-year-old boy, was found dead over thirty years ago. He had been sexually assaulted and strangled. Tests for blood grouping had failed but swabs were taken from the body and stored. These were reexamined in 1991 and, although once again no profile was obtained, semen stain samples were returned to the freezer.

Then in 1996 SGM profiling was used, and at last a DNA profile was obtained. Because of the new evidence the case was reopened and a match was made with Field with a probability of one in twenty million. He pleaded guilty to murder at the Old Bailey in November 2001. Judge Gerald Gordon said: "Advances in modern science techniques should stand as a warning that there is no hiding place for sexual and violent criminals."

THE DNA TIME CAPSULE

In 1981 Marion Croft's body is discovered on a cycle route near her home in Hampshire, U.K. She has been sexually assaulted and murdered. FSS scientists examine the scene in great detail but cannot link the evidence to a suspect. The forensic samples are stored on a laboratory slide in the hope that one day technology may improve and the killer can be identified. That day comes in 1999 when the slide is re-examined by the specialist DNA team at Trident Court using the DNA Low Copy Number (DNA LCN) method to find a full DNA profile of Marion's suspected killer from some of her clothing. The profile, however, does not find a match in the National DNA Database (NDNAD).

In 2001, during a routine upload of profiles onto the NDNAD, the FSS finds a match. The match is Tony Jasinskyj, a man who had been charged with a totally unrelated crime. The FSS scientists return to the laboratory slide and find a matching profile from Marion's clothing. Twenty years after the murder, Jasinskyj is found guilty.

THE DUKE OF EDINBURGH AND THE LAST TSARINA OF RUSSIA

In the 1970s a mass grave is discovered in Russia, which allegedly contains the bodies of Tsar Nicholas II and his family, who were assassinated in 1917. It is not until the fall of communism in 1991, however, that the remains are allowed to be thoroughly examined. The remains are in very poor condition and contain only small amounts of DNA, so examiners can only rely on mitochondrial DNA, which is passed through the female parent in each generation. Bizarrely, the donor with the best DNA match is Prince Philip, the husband of Queen Elizabeth II, who is a direct descendent of the Tsarina's sister. Through this process the bones are positively identified as those of the final Russian royal family.

THE RIGHTFUL HEIR

It is 1828 and we are in Nuremberg, Germany.

A disheveled young man of about sixteen, attired in peasant dress, stumbles into the street. He seems neither to understand nor be capable of speech. On his person the townsfolk discover letters stating that since infancy he has been kept in solitary confinement, existing on bread and water—his name is Kaspar.

Rumor abounds that Kaspar is actually the legitimate heir to the Dukedom of Baden but was abducted at birth in order for another son to receive the title. He is being cheated of his fortune and inheritance.

In December 1833 an unidentified assassin stabs Kaspar to death and the opportunity to solve the mystery is gone. Or has it? The FSS were asked to analyze bloodstains on Kaspar's clothes and see if a match could be obtained to living descendants of the Grand Duke of Baden, Karl Friedrich and his wife Stephanie de Beauharnais (Napoleon's stepdaughter). They used mitochondrial DNA sequencing to compare the samples obtained from the bloodstained clothing and the Baden family. This established, beyond doubt, that the rightful heir to the Baden family fortune was not Kaspar.

TRACKING DOWN A KILLER

Is an old murder investigation about to be solved? Police are on the trail of a killer who raped and strangled twenty-four-year-old Barbara Mayo in October 1970. She is found dumped near a junction of the M1 in Derbyshire, England; the police initiate the biggest murder investigation of the time but fail to hunt the killer down. It is now 1997 and new genetic fingerprinting technology inspires a reexamination. A list of two hundred and fifty possible suspects is compiled and the men are required to give DNA samples. Since then detectives have traveled to the U.S., Australia, Ireland, and New Zealand to get samples.

One of the suspects has moved to Canada—he is now quite elderly. Investigators say only a small number of men remain who have either emigrated or have proved untraceable. The detective superintendent leading the inquiry says that the suspect living in Canada has a mental condition, and therefore permission is needed from his doctors to obtain a DNA sample. The Canadian authorities are assisting in this respect.

WAITING IN THE WINGS

Time is running out for the murderer of an elderly woman found battered to death in her home in Northwest Leicestershire in April 1969. Annie Walker lives alone and by the time her body is discovered one thousand pounds (a great deal of cash in those days), which she had recently drawn from her bank account, is missing. After police are alerted by neighbors they break in and find her on the floor —she has been beaten to death with a blunt-edged instrument. Recently forensic experts have reexamined evidence collected at the crime scene and a DNA profile now exists which will positively identify the killer. All that is needed is a match.

A VAMPIRE'S KISS

It is November 2001 and the Isle of Anglesey in North Wales is appalled at the murder of a ninety-year-old woman at her home. The cause of death is obvious: she has suffered multiple stab wounds. But it is what happened postmortem that is most shocking. Her heart has been removed and a saucepan containing her blood has a lip print on the edge. Around the body objects are precisely placed, including a pair of crossed pokers and a candlestick. Are police hunting a vampire?

At the point of entry, a glass pane at the back door, forensic scientists find footwear prints in the smashed glass and are able to obtain an artist's impression of the killer's shoes—Levi trainers. Following up on a report of a suspect, police visit seventeen-year-old Matthew Hardman and he provides a buccal swab. A pair of Levi trainers is found— these are matched to the prints at the crime scene. A knife is also found but there are no visible signs of blood. A partial profile is produced with a match probability of one in a thousand but this, with the footwear match, is sufficient for Hardman to be arrested.

Further forensic work and DNA Low Copy Number testing on the knife's handle reveals DNA matching Hardman and the victim. The DNA match discrimination is now one in five million, rising to one in seventy-three million. Matthew Hardman is found guilty of murder in August 2002 and sentenced to life imprisonment.

Forensic Science— today and tomorrow

"Many more families can look forward to securing justice."

Paul Hackett, FSS, 2006

THE RIPPER'S SHADOW: LESSONS LEARNED

Peter Sutcliffe, "The Yorkshire Ripper," shocks everybody yet further when it is subsequently discovered that had a computer database used for storing salient information been in place and accessible to the police at the time he was an active killer, he may well have been stopped in his bloody tracks at a considerably earlier interval.

He was arrested nine times and released to kill due to lack of collated data; the establishment is keen to ensure that this lethal mistake is not repeated.

STATISTICAL "FINGERPRINT" OF THE WORLD'S WORST SERIAL MURDERER

In January 2000, Dr. Harold Shipman, a former family doctor in Manchester, U.K., is found guilty of murdering fifteen of his patients. It is suspected that he had killed more than two hundred and fifty others. Following his trial, the Chief Medical Officer for the country commissions an audit of Shipman's clinical practice for the years from his appointment in 1974 to his arrest in 1998. This shows how the deaths of Shipman's patients displayed a number of unusual characteristics with respect to time and place. Perhaps one of the most chilling was the early afternoon peak (during home visits) when the proportion of deaths for Shipman (fourteen percent at 2 p.m.) was about seven times higher than a comparison group of doctors.

To add to the tragedy for victims, their families, and other professionals was the fact that this information was already "in the system" all along but, of course, was not recorded, aggregated, tabulated, or graphed in a way that might have compelled investigation. The difference between life and death sometimes lies hidden in the data.

VIOLENT CRIMINAL APPREHENSION PROGRAM (VICAP)

The Violent Criminal Apprehension Program is overseen by the FBI and is designed to facilitate cooperation, communication, and coordination between U.S. law enforcement agencies. It is also set up to provide specialized support when investigating serious crimes. It pledges to identify, track, apprehend, and prosecute violent serial offenders.

VICAP is a data information center which operates on a nationwide scale. Using a wealth of available materials, including cataloged forensic evidence, the extensive program collects, collates, and analyzes crimes of a serious and violent nature—with additional scrutiny being paid to homicide and, in particular, serial homicide cases.

THE LIST

VICAP examines the following among other details:

- Solved or unsolved homicides or attempts, especially those that involve an abduction; are apparently random, motiveless, or sexually oriented; or are known or suspected to be part of a series;
- Missing persons, where the circumstances indicate a strong possibility of foul play and the victim is still missing;
- Unidentified dead bodies, where the manner of death is known or suspected to be homicide; and
- Sexual assault cases.

THE JILL DANDO INSTITUTE OF CRIME SCIENCE

A computerized system which predicts the likelihood of finding forensic evidence at crime scenes is hailed a success. Northants Police and University College London's Jill Dando Institute of Crime Science is responsible for the system's development. Based on data relating to house burglaries, the study produces correct predictions for forensic evidence in sixty-eight percent of cases.

SIMILARITIES WITH VICAP

In 1987 the British Home Office provides a Police National Computer, accessible by regional forces as a central criminal database. It is designed to allow a team of investigators to input and collate information such as witness information and interview statements for a simpler cross-referencing of information.

Similar in both design and objective to the FBI's VICAP (Violent Criminal Apprehension Program) it will lead to the arrest and conviction of many assailants, rapists and killers. It is called H.O.L.M.E.S. (Home Office Large Major Enquiry System). It is heralded as the "twenty-first-century detective" and by the following year much progress has been made with the facility. The huge system can store up to one hundred million words—or one gigabyte. It will later become instrumental in the apprehension of serial rapist and murderer John Duffy, along with scores of others.

ALONG COMES PNC2

NORTHWEST LONDON, DECEMBER 1991, AND HENDON POLICE STATION IS THE RECIPIENT OF THE SECOND-GENERATION HOME OFFICE POLICE NATIONAL COMPUTER—PNC2. POLICE FORCES THE LENGTH AND BREADTH OF THE U.K. ARE GRANTED TWENTY-FOUR-HOUR ACCESS TO ALL FINGERPRINT RECORDS AND VEHICULAR INFORMATION, FROM STOLEN AUTOMOBILES TO DISQUALIFIED DRIVERS AND THOSE SIMILARLY PENALIZED. THE SYSTEM IS ALSO SAID TO EMIT A WARNING SIGNAL WHEN AN IMPORTANT PIECE OF INFORMATION IS ATTACHED TO AN ALREADY-RECORDED FILE.

PNC2 HAS TWICE THE PROCESSING CAPACITY AND ALMOST FIVE TIMES THE MEMORY OF ITS H.O.L.M.E.S. PREDECESSOR. IT IS ABLE TO RESPOND TO EACH OF ITS APPROXIMATELY ONE HUNDRED AND TWENTY-FIVE THOUSAND INPUTTED DAILY QUERIES IN LESS THAN THREE SECONDS.

BIG FLOYD

This system operates similarly to H.O.L.M.E.S. and is used in the U.S. by the FBI to catalog a series of in-depth interviews with both the police and Justice Department as a means of establishing sequential questioning for use in major inquiries. The information is translated into language a computer will understand and then asked to reach conclusions based on all information available. Prime or most likely suspects will be selected based on such questions and matches. This saves the huge amount of time and effort a team of police officers would have to expend in questioning or physically locating suspects and witnesses when conducting a particular investigation.

FARWELL BRAIN FINGERPRINTING

In 1999 Dr. Lawrence Farwell develops the technique of "Farwell Brain Fingerprinting," a new computer-based method of identifying criminals by measuring brainwave responses to relevant pictures.

Today's advance in computers has greatly simplified tasks that were once considered very complicated. Three-dimensional laser scanners will soon replace microscopes. As technology advances into the future, forensic sciences like pathology, toxicology, anthropology, and odontology will follow.

READING LIPS

Some previously dubious types of evidence are becoming admissible in court. Three appeals about lip-reading from video film were recently given attention. The defense was unhappy, finding this new procedure unreliable. It argued that if the judge was not prepared to disallow it, he should at least instruct the jury on the possible frailty of such evidence.

The defense was ultimately unsuccessful in its argument, because the court begged to differ. It declared that lip-reading from a video was a genuine skill and good evidence. However it did advise as to "its limitations and the concomitant risk of error."

TV programs start to appear, portraying profiling as if it is some kind of supernatural alchemy. U.S. shows such as *The X-Files*, *CSI Investigation*, *Millennium*, and *Profiler*. British equivalaents like the hit series *Cracker* focus less on the fantastical side of profiling and more on the content as a hard-boiled science.

It is not possible to accurately foretell the future of forensic science but it seems probable that new developments in the gathering of data and its analysis, in addition to other fields like biotech and nanotech, will be instrumental in deciding how legal issues will be considered in the future.

THE ASSASSINATION OF JFK

The attempt to answer questions concerning the JFK assassination involves the use of a confocal microscope. This is cutting-edge technology and it seeks to establish a digital map of a more than forty-year-old Dallas police Dictaphone belt audio tape. The tape is presently in a bad condition, comprising only the sounds of chatter and background noise recorded on a police radio channel at the time of the shooting. This "reanimation" of a sound wave could effectively provide an answer to an important forensic issue in the case by creating an acoustic fingerprint for the gunshots that killed JFK.

OPPOSING OPINIONS

Ten medical experts give evidence at the trial of Darren Surutan in 2002. He is accused of the manslaughter of his partner, Sarah Lee. There are two points of contention: how many bruises are on Sarah's face, and had she received them in a fall (she is a known alcoholic) or has she been attacked by the defendant? Unfortunately the experts are unable to reach the same conclusions, giving contrary medical evidence. Because the jury, with insufficient guidance from the judge, are totally confused by the profoundly diverse opinions of the experts, the appeal court overturns Surutan's conviction and he walks free.

SCIENCE UP BEFORE THE COURT

SION JENKINS WAS FOUND GUILTY OF THE MURDER OF HIS FOSTER-DAUGHTER, BILLIE-JO, IN 1998 IN THE TOWN OF HASTINGS, EAST SUSSEX, ENGLAND. BILLIE-JO HAS BEEN BRUTALLY BEATEN TO DEATH WITH A METAL TENT SPIKE. BUT THIS CONVICTION IS SUBSEQUENTLY OVERTURNED WHEN THE COURT OF APPEAL DETERMINES THAT NEW FORENSIC EVIDENCE HAS MADE JENKINS'S CONVICTION UNSAFE. THE FORMER DEPUTY HEADMASTER LATER GIVES AN INTERVIEW ON BRITISH TELEVISION WHERE HE STRENUOUSLY AVOWS HIS INNOCENCE AND CONTESTS FORENSIC EVIDENCE USED AGAINST HIM IN HIS PREVIOUS TRIALS. WILL WE EVER KNOW IF HE IS TRULY THE KILLER OF BILLIE-JO?

OTHER MAJOR CASES, INCLUDING THOSE OF TWO MOTHERS SET FREE AFTER THEIR CONVICTIONS FOR KILLING THEIR BABIES WERE QUASHED, HAVE RAISED UNCERTAINTY IN THE U.K. ABOUT THE MANNER IN WHICH FORENSIC EVIDENCE IS USED. FOR THE FIRST TIME THE PUBLIC'S TRUST IN SCIENTIFIC WITNESSES IS IN PERIL. THE EXPERT WITNESS INSTITUTE HAS ADMITTED: "EXPERT EVIDENCE IS UNDER ATTACK..."

THE FUTURE

Perhaps this will always be the case, but without such expert evidence, given freely in encompassing forensic science's potent and decisive spectrum, where will the legal system be in its battle to protect the public in effectively and fairly punishing the wrongdoer? Many more innocent people who come under attack from predators will surely advocate its continuance. Where there are convictions to be secured, forensic science will continue to prove a most valuable ally.

FSS BREAKTHROUGH

It is October 2006 and The Forensic Science Service (FSS) is researching a new technique which can interpret previously unintelligible DNA samples. The system will permit scientists to differentiate between DNA samples touched by more than one person or where only minute or poor-quality material is found. The new technique, entitled "DNAboost," could solve innumerable "cold" cases or indeed impact upon future cases. Paul Hackett of FSS says, "We think we can boost the success rate of our ability to pass on new leads to the police by around ten percent."

INDEX